STUDENT WORKBOOK

SHOW WHAT YOU KNOW® ON THE

TAKS

FOR GRADE 5

D1397364

grade 5

PREPARATION FOR
THE TEXAS ASSESSMENT
OF KNOWLEDGE AND SKILLS

Show What You Know® Publishing

NAME

Published by:
Show What You Know® Publishing
A Division of Englefield & Associates, Inc.
P.O. Box 341348
Columbus, OH 43234-1348
Phone: 614-764-1211
www.showwhatyouknowpublishing.com
www.passthetaks.com

Printed in the United States of America
05 04 03   20 19 18 17 16 15 14 13 12 11 10 9 8 7 6 5 4 3 2 1

ISBN: 1-59230-014-6

Acknowledgements

Show What You Know® Publishing acknowledges the following for their efforts in making this assessment material available for Texas students, parents, and teachers.

Cindi Englefield, President/Publisher
Eloise Boehm-Sasala, Vice President/Managing Editor
Mercedes Baltzell, Production Editor
Scott D. Stuckey, Editor
Lainie Burke, Editor/Graphic Design
Jennifer Harney, Illustrator/Cover Designer
Kathie Christian, Proofreader

About the Contributors

The content of this book was written BY teachers FOR teachers and students and was designed specifically for the Texas Assessment of Knowledge and Skills (TAKS) for Grade 5. Contributions to the Science, Reading, and Mathematics sections of this book were also made by the educational publishing staff at Show What You Know® Publishing. Dr. Jolie S. Brams, a clinical child and family psychologist, is the contributing author of the Tackling Test Anxiety and Test-Taking Strategies chapters of this book. Without the contributions of these people, this book would not be possible.

Table of Contents

Introduction

The purpose of the Texas Assessment of Knowledge and Skills (TAKS) is to measure student learning. Throughout the school year, students are exposed to a wide variety of concepts from a range of disciplines, only some of which are tested by the TAKS. Yet it is important that all Texas Essential Knowledge and Skills (TEKS) be taught in order to ensure that students have a well-rounded understanding of the fifth-grade curriculum. Students who have been taught the elements of the TEKS curriculum will have been exposed to all that is assessed by the TAKS. Nonetheless, students will benefit from the review of key details as they prepare to take this assessment.

The *Show What You Know® on the TAKS for Grade 5, Student Workbook* is designed to help students better understand the types of information they will see on the TAKS. This book will help students review important elements assessed by the TAKS; it is not a substitute for continuous teaching and learning, which take place both in and outside the classroom. But, as with any assessment, it is a good idea to review principles that have been taught and learned prior to taking the TAKS.

Show What You Know® on the TAKS for Grade 5 includes many features that will benefit students as they prepare for the TAKS.

The first two chapters—Tackling Test Anxiety and Test-Taking Strategies—were written especially for fifth graders. Tackling Test Anxiety offers advice on how to reduce anxious feelings about tests, and Test-Taking Strategies gives strategies students can use to do their best on tests.

The Science, Reading, and Mathematics chapters of this book will introduce students to the types of questions they will answer on the TAKS. In addition, there are two assessment tests per subject. These tests will help students become familiar with the look and feel of the TAKS. Each assessment test is a great opportunity for students to practice their test-taking skills.

For easy reference, this Student Workbook correlates with the *Show What You Know® on the TAKS for Grade 5, Parent/Teacher Edition* (sold separately).

Tackling Test Anxiety

Worry Less about Tests

Lots of students worry about taking tests, so, if you are a test worrier, you are not alone! Many of your classmates and friends also have fearful feelings about tests, but they usually do not share their feelings. Keeping feelings to yourself is not a good idea because it just makes things worse. You may feel you are the only person with a problem and there is no one out there to help, but that is not true! Be brave! When you talk to your parents, teachers, and friends about your test-taking worries, you will feel better. You will find out that other people (even your teachers and parents) have felt worried, nervous, or scared about taking tests. You will then have other people on your team to battle the test monster!

When students feel nervous, worried, and scared, it sometimes seems there is no way out. This is also not true! Everyone can feel calm about taking tests. You don't have to be the smartest student, the most popular kid, or the fastest athlete to be a brave test taker. You just need to be willing to try; you will be amazed at how much better you will feel!

What is it Like to Have "Test Anxiety?"

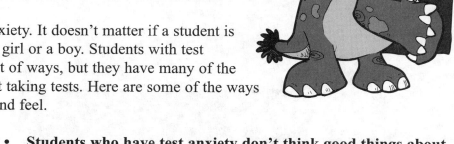

One definition of the word *anxiety* is "feeling anxious, worried, and scared." When students feel this way about taking tests, it is called "test anxiety." In this chapter, the phrase "test anxiety" will be used a lot. Just remember that no matter what you call it, you will learn how to beat the test monster!

All sorts of students have test anxiety. It doesn't matter if a student is tall or short, shy or friendly, or a girl or a boy. Students with test anxiety might be different in a lot of ways, but they have many of the same thoughts and feelings about taking tests. Here are some of the ways students with test anxiety think and feel.

- **Students who have test anxiety don't think good things about themselves.**
  Instead of thinking about all they know, these students spend most of their time thinking about what they don't know. When their minds become filled with lists of what they don't know, there isn't any room left for remembering what they have learned and all they can do! It is like their minds are closets filled with only bad things, never good ones. Imagine if you filled your closet at home with broken toys, worn-out clothes, crumpled-up papers, and all sorts of garbage. You would open up your closet and say to yourself, "Boy, my life is awful!" You would ignore all the other good things you might have in your room, as well as in your life. You can bet you would not be feeling very good about yourself.

- **Students who have test anxiety "exaggerate."**
  Exaggerating means "making things bigger than they are." While exaggeration makes books and movies exciting and interesting, exaggeration makes test anxiety worse. Worried thoughts grow like a mushroom out of control! "Oh no! I don't know how to do this type of math problem. See, I can't do anything! I am the worst math student ever, and I'm sure my life will be a total mess!" Students with test anxiety make the worst out of situations and imagine all kinds of things that will not really happen. Their thoughts get scarier and scarier, and their futures look darker and darker. The more these students exaggerate, the more anxious and worried they become.

- **Students who have test anxiety sometimes do not feel well.**

  It is important to remember your mind and body work together! What goes on in your mind can change how your body feels, and how your body feels can change what goes on in your thinking. When your mind is filled with worries about tests, your body may also "worry." You may feel your heart jumping, your stomach might hurt, your hands might become sweaty, your head may hurt, or you might even feel that you can't breathe very well. Feeling bad gets in the way of "doing your best on tests." Feeling bad also makes students feel even more anxious. They say to themselves, "My heart is really beating fast, and my hands are shaking. See, I'm such a mess; I'll fail that test!" Then, they just become more worried and more anxious. Some students with test anxiety miss a lot of school, not because they are lazy, but because they believe they really are not feeling well. Sadly, the more school they miss, the more they fall behind, and the more nervous they feel. Their physical feelings keep them from enjoying school and facing the test monster.

- **Students who have test anxiety want to escape.**

  When some students are anxious, they feel so bad that they will do anything to stay away from that feeling. They run away from problems, especially tests. Some students try to get away from tests by missing school or maybe by going to the nurse's office. This does not solve any problems because the more a student is away from the classroom, the harder the school work becomes. In the end, students who try to get away feel even worse than they did before, and they will have to take the test later on anyway. Running away from problems that cause anxiety may seem to make you feel better for a while, but it does not solve problems or make them go away.

- **Students who have test anxiety do not show what they know on tests.**

  For students who are feeling worried and anxious, it's really hard to make good decisions! Instead of concentrating on the test, planning out their answers, and using what they know, students who have test anxiety "blank out." They stare at the paper and see that no answer is there! They become "stuck" and cannot move on. Some students come up with the wrong answer because their worries get in the way of reading directions carefully or thinking about their answers. Their minds are running in a hundred different directions, and none of those directions seems to be getting them anywhere. They forget to use what they know, and they also forget to use study skills that would help them do their best. Imagine your mind as a safe. Inside the safe are all the answers to tests and a whole lot of knowledge about school work. However, anxiety has taken away the key! Even though the answers are there, the key is gone! Your mind is racing and you can't think clearly about where you put the key! All that knowledge is trapped in there with nowhere to go. When students feel calmer about taking tests, their wonderful minds open up, and exciting ideas come pouring out!

Are You One of These "Test Anxious" Fifth Graders?

As you have seen, students with test anxiety think bad things about themselves, feel sick some of the time, and forget how to do well on tests. Do any of the kids described below remind you of yourself?

Stay-Away Stephanie

Stephanie's thoughts tell her it is better to stay away from anything that might be hard to do, especially tests. Stephanie is a good girl, but she is always in trouble for trying to avoid tests. Sometimes, Stephanie will beg her mother to allow her to stay home on test days. When that doesn't work, she will refuse to get out of bed or to catch the bus to school! You'd better believe she gets in trouble for that! Sometimes, at school, she will hide in the bathroom or go to the school nurse when test-taking time comes. Stephanie truly believes there is nothing worse than taking a test. She has so much anxiety that she forgets about all the problems that will happen when she stays away from her responsibilities. Stay-Away Stephanie feels less nervous when she stays away from tests, but she never learns to face her fears.

Worried Wendy

Wendy is the type of fifth grader who always looks for the worst thing to happen. Her mind is filled with all types of worried thoughts. She exaggerates everything bad and forgets about everything good. Her mind races a mile a minute with all sorts of thoughts and ideas about tests, all of them bad. The more she thinks, the worse she feels, and then her problems become huge! Instead of just worrying about a couple of difficult questions on a test, she finds herself thinking about failing the whole test, being made fun of by her friends, being grounded by her parents, and never going to college. She completely forgets that her parents are really nice and not strict, that her friends like her for a whole bunch of reasons, and that doing poorly on one test is not going to ruin her life. Wendy is always watching and waiting for the worst thing to happen. She spends her time worrying instead of figuring out how to do well.

Critical Chris

Chris is the type of fifth grader who spends all of his time putting himself down. No matter what happens, he always feels he has failed. While some people hold grudges against others, Chris holds grudges against himself. Even if he makes little mistakes, he can never forget them. Chris has had many good things happen in his life, and he has been successful many times. Unfortunately, Chris forgets the good and only remembers the bad. If he gets a "C+" on a test, he can't remember the times he earned "As" and "Bs." When he gets a "B+" on a test, he says to himself, "I made a lot of stupid mistakes, so I didn't get an 'A.'" He never compliments himself by thinking, "I did AWESOME by getting a 'B+.'" If Chris liked himself better, he would have less test anxiety.

4

Victim Vince

Most fifth graders know it is important to take responsibility for themselves, but Vince wants to blame everything on others. He can't take responsibility for himself at all. He thinks everything is someone else's fault and constantly complains about friends, parents, school work, and especially about tests. He thinks his teachers are unfair and life is against him. Vince does not feel there is anything he can do to prepare for the TAKS or to help himself in any other way. Because he does not try to learn test-taking skills or understand why he is afraid, he just keeps feeling angry, sad, and worried.

Perfect Pat

Every fifth grader needs to try his or her best, but no one should try as much as Pat! Pat studies and studies, and, when she is not studying, she is worrying. No matter what she does, it's never enough. She will write book reports over and over and will study for tests until she is exhausted. Trying hard is fine, but, no matter what Pat does, she feels she has not done enough. She feels worried because she cannot stop thinking there is always more to know. Her anxiety gets higher and higher, but this does not mean she does better and better on tests. In fact, the more anxious she gets, the harder tests become. Then, when she does not do well on a test, she just wants to study more and more. What a mess! Pat should spend more time learning how to study and find time to relax.

How Can I Feel Calmer about Tests?

Test anxiety is a very powerful feeling that makes students feel they are weak and helpless. Nervous feelings can be so powerful that it sometimes seems there is nothing you can do to stop them. Worries seem to take over your mind and body and leave you feeling like you are going to lose the test-anxiety battle for sure.

The good news is that there are many things you can do to win the battle over test anxiety! If you can learn these skills in elementary school, you are on the road to success in middle school and for all the other challenges in your life.

- **Don't let yourself feel alone.**
  Although sometimes it is fun to curl up in bed and read a book by yourself, most of the time it is not very much fun to be alone! This is really true when you are feeling anxious or worried. Talking to your friends, parents, and teachers about worried feelings, especially feelings about test taking, can really help you feel better. Having test-taking worries does not mean there is something wrong with you! You might be surprised to find out that many of your friends and classmates also feel anxious about tests. You might even be more surprised to learn that your parents and teachers also had test anxiety when they were younger. They know what you are going through and are there to help you.

- **There is more than one side to any story!**

  Most fifth graders have heard a parent or teacher tell them, "There is more than one side to any story." It is easy to get in the habit of thinking about situations in a bad way instead of thinking happy thoughts. You can help yourself feel better about your life and about taking tests by training yourself to think about things from a happy point of view.

  Think about a can of soda. Get out a piece of paper and a pen or pencil. Now, draw a line down the middle of the paper. On one side, write the heading "All the bad things about this can of soda." On the other side of the paper, write the heading "All the good things about this can of soda." Fill in the chart with your thoughts about the can of soda. When you are finished, your chart might look like the one below.

All the bad things about this can of soda	All the good things about this can of soda
Not an attractive color	*Easy-to-read lettering*
It's getting warm	*Nice to have something to drink*
Not much in the can	*Inexpensive*
Has a lot of sugar	*Recyclable aluminum cans*

Look how easy it is to write down either good things or bad things about a silly can of soda! That can of soda is not good or bad; it's just a can of soda. You can either look at it in a good way, or you can think about everything bad that comes to your mind. Doesn't the same thing hold true for tests? Tests are not good or bad in themselves. Tests are just a way to challenge you and to see how much you know. Studying for tests can be boring and can take up a lot of free time, but you can also learn a lot when you study. Studying can make you feel great about yourself. Even if you

make some mistakes on a test, you can learn from those mistakes. You can also look at your test results and compliment yourself on how much you have learned. The way you think about tests has a lot to do with how well you will be able to "show what you know." Students who have good thoughts about tests are less anxious and do better. Students who always have bad thoughts and feelings about tests usually do not do as well as they should.

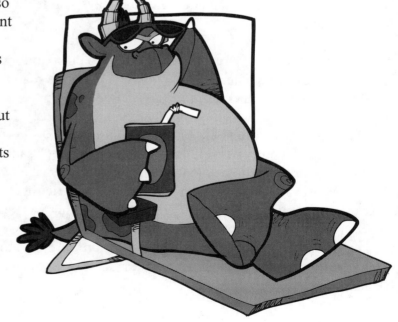

- **Think good things about yourself!**
The better you feel about yourself, the better you will do on tests! This does not mean you should go around boasting and bragging to your friends about how wonderful you are! What helps most on tests is to think about all the good things you have done and learned in your past. Remind yourself of those things when you are studying for tests or even when you are taking a test.

Thinking good things about yourself takes practice. The chart below is divided into three parts. For the first part, fill in as many sentences as you can that describe "Why I Am Special." In the example below, this fifth grader has already filled in "I am very kind to animals" and "I have a good sense of humor." Next, you want to remember what you have done in your life. Make a section on the chart that reads "Things I Have Done." The fifth grader below has started his chart by remembering "I helped paint my room" and "I got a library award." Don't forget to ask your family to remind you about who you are and what you have done. Make believe you are a news reporter working on a story. Interview your parents, grandparents, aunts, uncles, brothers, sisters, or anyone else who can remind you of all the good things you have done and the good person you are. Make sure to add those to your chart. This fifth grader's grandfather told him he is "smiley." Keep a chart like this in a special place where you can look at it if you are feeling anxious about tests or not very good about yourself. Reading it will make you feel better. When you feel good about yourself or when something good happens, add it to the chart! You will be amazed at what a wonderful person you are. The better you feel about yourself, the better you will be able to "show what you know" in school and on tests.

Why I Am Special	Things I Have Done	What My Family Thinks
I am very kind to animals.	*I helped paint my room.*	*Grandpa thinks I'm "smiley."*
I have a good sense of humor.	*I got a library award.*	

- **Everything is not a disaster!**
If you always think a disaster is about to happen, it is called "catastrophizing." A catastrophe is a disaster. It is when something terrible happens. When students catastrophize about tests, their minds go on and on thinking about terrible scenes of failure. It is like a horror movie about school, but it is worse. It is real life!

When students stop themselves from catastrophizing, their test anxiety becomes much less noticeable. When you feel yourself catastrophizing, make yourself stop. Tell yourself, "STOP! None of this is going to happen. Tests might be hard, but they are not going to be the end of the world." Disasters have a way of getting out of hand, so, the sooner you can stop yourself thinking those thoughts, the better off you will be. Disaster thoughts get you nowhere; they only make you more anxious. The most important part is that they are not true! No matter how you do on the TAKS or on other tests in the fifth grade, your life will go on, and it will be just fine!

- **Don't make "should" statements.**

Students make themselves anxious when they think they "should" do everything! They feel they "should" be as smart as everyone else, they "should" study more, and they "should" not feel anxious about tests. All of those thoughts are pretty ridiculous! Not everyone is going to be as smart as the next person, and you do not have to study until you drop to do well on tests. Instead of kicking yourself for not being perfect, it is better to set some reasonable goals about studying and school work. This will help you get better grades on tests and feel happier in your life.

- **Take out those bad thoughts and put in good ones!**

If you are thinking good thoughts, it's impossible to think bad ones! People who are worried or anxious can become happier and more relaxed by thinking good thoughts. Even when something scary is happening, such as a visit to the dentist, thinking "positive thoughts" is very helpful. If you are thinking about something that is good or positive, it is almost impossible to think of something that is bad or negative. Keep this in mind when test anxiety starts to become a bother.

Try using some of these thoughts when you find yourself becoming worried.

<u>Thoughts of success</u> – Thinking "I can do it" thoughts chases away thoughts of failure. Imagining times when you were successful, such as doing well in a soccer game or figuring out a complicated brain teaser, will help you realize you can be successful. On the morning of the test, think positive thoughts. Think about arriving at school and feeling sure that you will do well on the test. Imagine closing your eyes before the test, breathing deeply, relaxing, and remembering all that you have learned. When you think about success, you will achieve success! During the test, remind yourself that you have been successful in the past and can do well in the future and on this test. This will chase away your worried thoughts.

<u>Relaxing thoughts</u> – You can't be worried and relaxed at the same time! Thinking about a time when you felt comfortable and happy can chase away your worries. Think about a time that you went swimming, had a pillow fight at a sleep over, or went out with your family for a huge ice-cream sundae. Soon, you will find yourself thinking about the good things in life, not the worries that trouble you.

<u>Thoughts about beating the test monster</u> –
When you get ready to take a test, imagine you are in battle with an ugly test monster! Think about the hard work that you do to study and the good things about you. Imagine there are huge swords chasing away the test monster. Imagine the test monster running for his life as you chase away your worries and "show what you know" on the test! Even though it might sound silly, it works!

8

- **Relaxing helps chase away anxiety.**

Just as you can calm your mind, it is also important for you to relax your body. When you have test anxiety, your muscles can become stiff. In fact, your whole body might become tense. Taking deep breaths before a test and letting them out slowly as well as relaxing muscles in your body are very helpful ways to feel less anxious. You may find that not only does relaxation help you on tests, but it is also helpful for other challenging situations and for feeling healthy overall. Athletes, astronauts, and surgeons all use relaxation to help them perform their best. Here are some other methods you can try. You might also discover a different method that works well for you. Some methods will work better than others for you, so be sure to use the methods that are best for you.

Listen to music – It probably doesn't matter what type of music you listen to as long as it makes you feel good about yourself. You might want to listen to music while you study, but, if it disturbs your concentration, it will not be helpful. Listening to music when you go to sleep the night before a test or in the morning while you get ready for school may also help you relax.

Develop a routine – Some people find it relaxing to have a set routine to go through each morning. Having a calm morning and a nice breakfast before you take a test such as the TAKS is always helpful. Rushing around on the morning of a test not knowing what to do next is only going to make your worries worse! When students rush and feel out of control, they begin to think, "I'll never get everything done" and, "This day is starting out terribly!" Ask your family to be respectful of your routine and tell them how they can help you be more successful. This might include giving you an extra hand in getting ready the morning of the test or making sure you get to school on time.

Take care of yourself – Everyone is busy. Most fifth graders are involved in all sorts of activities including sports, music, and helping around the house. They also love their free time and can stay out for hours skateboarding or just hanging around with their friends. Sometimes, they are so busy they forget to eat breakfast or they don't get enough sleep. Eating and sleeping right are important, especially before a test like the TAKS. Even you are not a big breakfast eater, try to find something that you like to eat, and get in the habit of eating breakfast. When you do not eat right, you feel shaky, you have a hard time thinking, and you have more anxiety. Being tired does not help either. Try to get in the habit of going to bed early enough every night so that you feel fresh and rested for the TAKS or other tests in school. Your body will be more relaxed if it is well-fed and well-rested.

Practice relaxing your body – No matter what method of relaxation you find works best for you, it is very important to practice that method so you feel comfortable with it. Practicing your relaxation method will help you during times when you are anxious, because you will know what to do to calm yourself without having to worry about it; it will become your natural response to the stressful things around you.

- **Learn to use study skills.**
  There is a chapter in this book that will help you learn test-taking strategies. The more you know about taking tests successfully, the calmer you will feel. Knowledge is power! Practice test-taking strategies to reduce your test anxiety.

- **Congratulate yourself during the test.**
  Instead of thinking, "I've only done five problems, and I have so many pages to go" or, "I knew three answers, but one mixed me up," think about how well you have done so far! Tell yourself, "I've gotten some answers right, so I bet I can do more." If you concentrate on the good things you are doing during a test, you will stay calm and allow yourself to do more good things on that test.

- **Don't get down on yourself for feeling a little worried.**
  You are not alone if you feel worried about tests; **everyone** feels a little worried about tests. Don't be hard on yourself! If you keep telling yourself, "I'm worried, so I'll never do well," then the worst will probably happen! Instead, tell yourself, "Lots of kids get anxious. Let me just calm myself down, and I will do fine." It is important to remember that being a little worried is natural. If you know that worrying happens to everyone, it will help you defeat your anxiety and become calm and focused on the test you are taking. Remember, you are not alone in your test-taking worries!

Test-Taking Strategies

You Can Do Your Best on Tests!

Most students want to do their best on tests. Tests are an important way for teachers to know how well students are doing and for students to understand how much progress they are making in school. The Texas Assessment of Knowledge and Skills (TAKS) helps schools find out how well students are learning. This helps teachers and principals make their schools even better. You can do the best job possible in "showing what you know" by learning how to be a good test taker.

It is not possible to do a good job without the right tools. Test-taking strategies are tools to help you "show what you know" on tests. Everyone needs good tools to fix a problem. It doesn't matter whether the problem is taking the TAKS or fixing a broken bicycle; without good tools, it's hard to be a success! Think about what would happen if your bicycle breaks and you do not have the right tools to fix it. You might know a lot about bicycles, but you can't "show what you know" unless you have the correct tools to fix it. You might know that the bolts on your wheels have to be put on very tight, but how can you do that without good tools to help?

Tools are not "tricks." Using good test-taking strategies is not cheating. The best students are not geniuses; they have learned to use good test-taking strategies. They learned what they need to do to "show what they know" when they are taking tests. You can learn these test-taking strategies, too!

Test-Taking Tools That You Can Use!

Be an active learner.

You might have heard the comment, "He soaks up knowledge like a sponge." Actually, the opposite of that idea is true. Although sponges soak up a lot of water just by lying around, your brain does not work that way with information. Just because you are sitting in a classroom does not mean you are going to learn anything simply by being there. Students learn when they participate during the school day. This is called "active learning." Active learners pay attention to what is being said. They ask themselves questions about what they hear. Active learners enjoy school, learn a lot, feel good about themselves, and usually do better on tests.

It takes time and practice to become an active learner. If you are the type of student who is easily bored or always frustrated, it is going to take some practice to use your classroom time differently. Ask yourself the following questions.

- Do I look at the teacher when he or she is talking?

- Do I pay attention to what is being said?

- Do I have any questions or ideas about what the teacher is saying?

- Do I listen to what my classmates are saying and think about their ideas?

- Do I work with others to try to solve difficult problems?

- Do I look at the clock and wonder what time school will be over, or do I enjoy what is happening during the school day and wonder how much I can learn?

- Do I think about how my school work might help me now or in the future?

The more you actively participate in school, the more you will learn and the better you will do on tests. Think about Kristen!

There was a young girl named Kristen,
Who was bored and wouldn't listen.
She didn't train,
To use her smart brain,
And never knew what she was missing!

Do not rely on luck.

Although sometimes it's fun to believe in luck, luck alone is not going to help you do well on the TAKS or other tests. You might know a student who feels better having a lucky coin in his or her pocket or wearing a lucky pair of shoes when taking a test. That is fine, but the best way to do well on a test is to take responsibility for yourself by taking the time and effort to do well. It is easy to say to yourself, "It's not my fault that I did poorly. It's just not my lucky day." If you believe in luck and not in your own skills, you aren't going to get very far! Students who feel they have no control over what happens to them usually receive poor grades and do not do well on tests. Don't be like Chuck!

There was a cool boy named Chuck,
Who thought taking tests was just luck.
He never prepared,
He said "I'm not scared,"
When his test scores appear, he should duck!

Do your best every day!

Fifth grade is not an easy year. All of a sudden, the work seems really hard! Fifth-grade teachers are getting their students ready for middle school and are giving them more responsibility (and probably a lot more homework!). Sometimes, it feels like you could never learn all you need to know to do well on the TAKS. Many students begin to feel hopeless, and, sometimes, it seems easy just to give up.

Students are surprised when they find out that, if they just set small goals for themselves, they can learn an amazing amount! Do you know that if you learn just one new fact every day of the year, at the end of the year, you will know 365 new facts? Think about what happens if you learn three new facts every day. At the end of the year, you will have learned 1,095 new facts. When you think about the TAKS or other tests that you have to take in school, try to think about what you can learn step by step and day by day. If you try every day, you will be surprised at how all of this learning adds up to make you one of the smartest fifth graders ever. Think about Ray!

There was a smart boy named Ray,
Who learned something new every day.
He was pretty impressed,
With what his mind could possess
His excellent scores were his pay!

Get to know the TAKS!

Most fifth graders are probably pretty used to using their own CD players, televisions, or alarm clocks. They know how to use all of the controls to get the loudest sound, the clearest picture, or the early wake up! Now, imagine you are asked to use some electronic equipment that you have never seen before. You would probably think to yourself, "Where is the volume control? How do I put channels in memory? I don't even know how to change the channels to begin with! How do I put the battery in this thing?" You would probably spend a lot of time trying to figure out how everything works.

Now, think about the TAKS. It will be very hard to do a good job on the TAKS if you've never seen that test before. Although the TAKS is a test, it is probably different from tests you have taken before. Getting to know the TAKS is a great test-taking tool. The more you get used to the types of questions on the TAKS and how to record your answers, the better you will do. You will also save yourself time, time you can use to answer the questions instead of trying to understand how they work. Think about Sue!

There was a kid named Sue,
Who thought her tests look very new.
"I never saw this before!
How'd I get a bad score?"
If she'd have practiced, she'd have had more of a clue!

Read the directions and questions carefully!

Most fifth graders think directions are pretty boring. Fifth graders have already been in school for at least six years. Many of them think they have heard every direction ever invented, and it is easy for them to "tune out" directions. Not paying careful attention to the question that is being asked is a very bad idea. Do not tell yourself, "These directions are just like other directions I've had many times before," or, "I'm not really going to take time to read these directions because I know what the question will be." The directions on the TAKS are not there to trick or to confuse you, but you cannot do well on this test if you do not read the directions and questions carefully. Read the directions and questions slowly. Repeat them to yourself. Ask yourself if what you are reading makes sense. These are powerful test-taking strategies. Think about Fred!

There was a nice boy named Fred,
Who forgot almost all that he read.
The directions were easy,
But he said "I don't need these."
He should have read them instead.

Know how to fill in those answer bubbles!

By the time you are in the fifth grade, you have probably filled in answer bubbles on tests before. Remember, if you don't fill them in correctly, your answer will not be counted. Don't forget that a computer will be "reading" your answers. If you do not fill in the answer bubble dark enough, or if you use a check mark or dot, your smart thinking will not be counted! Look at the examples given below.

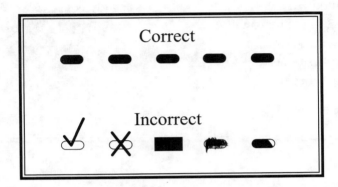

Some answers on the Science and Mathematics sections of the TAKS require you to fill in a griddable item. For the griddable items, you will need to solve a math problem and fill in a "response grid" that contains a number answer. An example of a griddable item is shown below. It is very important that you take time to study response grids and to practice filling in answers on the grid. Answer boxes are boxes where you write your answer. Number bubbles are the places where you mark the correct answer by filling in "bubbles" under the numbers that you wrote. When you are asked to use a response grid, remember the following.

- Always write your answer first in the answer boxes above the bubbles.

- Make sure you print only one number in each answer box.

- After you have written your number answer in with your pencil, you may then fill in the bubbles that are below each answer box.

- Make sure to keep everything in line. Do not fill in two answer bubbles under one number. Make sure there is only one filled-in bubble under each answer box. Make sure you fill in each bubble with a solid black mark that completely fills the bubble. Remember, although computers may be smart, they can't read your mind!

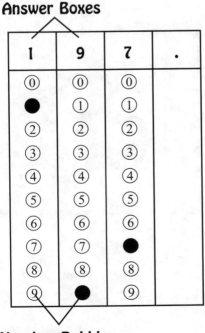

Learning how to fill in response grids takes practice, practice, and more practice! It may not be how you are used to writing math answers, but it is one way to give a right answer on the TAKS. Think about Kay!

A stubborn girl named Kay,
Liked to answer questions her own way.
So her marked answer bubbles,
Gave her all sorts of troubles.
Her test scores ruined her day!

Speeding through the test does not help!

The TAKS gives students enough time to read and to answer all the questions. There will always be some students who finish the TAKS more quickly than others, but this does not mean their scores will be better. It does not matter whether you finish quickly or slowly. As long as you take your time, prepare for the TAKS, pay attention to the test, and use some of the skills you have learned in this book, you should do just fine. No one will get a better score just because he or she finishes first! Speeding through a test question or racing through the whole TAKS does not help you do well. In fact, students do their best when they work carefully, not too slow and not too fast. Think about Liz!

There was a student named Liz,
Who sped through her test like a whiz.
She thought she should race
At a very fast pace,
But it caused her to mess up her quiz.

Answer every question!

Did you know there is no penalty for guessing on the TAKS? That is really good news! That means you have a one out of four chance of getting a multiple-choice question right, even if you just close your eyes and guess. For every four questions you guess, you probably will get 25% (one out of four) of the questions right. This means it is better to guess than to leave questions blank. Guessing by itself is not going to make you a star on the TAKS, but leaving multiple-choice questions blank is not going to help you either.

It is always better to study hard and to be prepared, but everyone has to guess at some time or another. Some people do not like to guess because they are afraid of choosing the wrong answer, but there is nothing wrong with guessing if you can't figure out the correct answer. Think about Jess!

There was a smart girl named Jess,
Who thought it was useless to guess.
If a question was tough,
She just gave up.
This only added to her stress.

Some students use a "code" to help them make good answering choices. Using your pencil in the test booklet, you can mark the following codes next to each multiple-choice question. This will help you decide what answer will be best. It will even help you to guess! Read through the codes below.

- (+) Putting a "plus sign" by a choice means you think that choice is more correct than others.
- (?) Putting a "question mark" by a choice means you are not sure if that is the correct answer, but it could be. You don't want to rule it out completely.
- (−) Putting a "minus sign" by a choice means you are sure it is the wrong answer. If you were going to guess, you wouldn't guess that answer.

Remember, it is fine to write in your test booklet. Your pencil is a powerful tool! Use it well. Think about Dwight!

There was a smart kid named Dwight,
Who marked choices that looked right.
He'd put a plus sign,
Or a dash or a line,
Now the whole world knows he is bright!

Do not get stuck on one question.

One of the biggest mistakes that students make on the TAKS is to get stuck on one question. The TAKS gives you many chances to show all that you have learned. If you do not know the answer to one or two questions, your test score will not be ruined. If you spend all of your time worrying and wondering about one or two hard questions, you will not give yourself the chance to answer the questions you do know.

If you feel "stuck" on a question, make yourself move on. You can come back to this question later and you may be able to answer it then. This is because one question or answer may remind you of how to answer another question that seemed difficult before. Also, when you start answering questions successfully and stop being "stuck," you will feel calmer and better about yourself. Then, when you go back to the hard question, you will have the confidence you need to do well. Do not tie up all of your time on one difficult question! No one knows all of the answers on the TAKS. Just circle the question that is giving you trouble and come back to it later. Think about Von!

There was a sweet girl named Von,
Who got stuck and just couldn't go on.
She'd sit there and stare,
But the answer wasn't there,
Before she knew it, all the time was gone.

Use your common sense!

You know a lot more than what you have learned in school. Most people solve problems using what they know from their daily lives as well as many things they have learned in school. When you take the TAKS, you should use everything you have learned in school, but you should also use what you have learned outside the classroom to help you answer questions correctly. This is called "using common sense."

Think about a mathematics question that has to do with baking cakes. You are asked to figure out the "median" temperature at which cakes should be baked. You quickly figure out the answer, and your number shows "3,500° F." Does that seem right to you? If you think about what you know, you know you have never seen 3,500° F on the oven in your house. How could this answer be right? You go back and look at your answer and realize you put a decimal in the wrong place. The correct answer is "350° F." Now you have used your common sense to figure out a correct answer. Although the mathematics question might have been difficult at first, your common sense saved the day. Think about Drew!

There was a boy named Drew,
Who forgot to use what he knew.
He had lots of knowledge,
He could have been in college!
But his right answers were few.

Always recheck your work!

Everyone makes mistakes. The most mistakes are made when students feel a little worried or rushed. Checking your work is very important. Careless mistakes can easily lead to a wrong answer, even when you have figured out the answer correctly. Always read a paragraph over again if there is something you do not understand. Look to see if there is something you forgot. In the Mathematics section, look at your work to make sure you did not mix one number up with another. Check to make sure your addition, subtraction, multiplication, and division problems are all lined up neatly and are easy to read. If your numbers seem messy, you might have made a mistake. If an answer does not seem to make sense, go back and reread the question or recheck your work. Think about Cath and Jen!

A smart young lady named Cath,
Always forgot to recheck her math.
She thought she was done,
But wrote eleven instead of one!
When her test score comes she won't laugh.

There was a quick girl named Jen,
Who read stuff once and never again.
It would have been nice,
If she read it twice.
Her scores would be better then!

Pay attention to yourself and not to others.

What matters on the TAKS is how you do, not how your friends are doing. When you are taking a test, it is easy to look around the room and wonder how your friends are doing. This is a waste of time. Instead, use your time and energy to "show what you know."

If you find your attention wandering away from the test, give yourself a little break. Think good thoughts about the TAKS and try to put scary thoughts out of your mind. Stretch your arms and feet or move around a little bit in your chair. Anything you can do to pay better attention is a great test-taking strategy. Think about Kirk!

There was a boy named Kirk,
Who thought of everything but his work.
He stared in the air,
And wiggled in his chair.
When his test scores come he won't look!

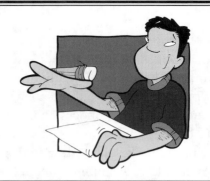

If you do not understand something, speak up!

No one wants to look "dumb." Some students think that, if they ask questions about school work or the TAKS, their classmates will think they are "dumb." There is nothing wrong with asking questions. The TAKS can be a complicated test. Asking questions about the test will help you do your best. You might be surprised to learn your classmates might have the same questions that you do but are afraid to ask. Don't sit on your hands! Instead, raise them to ask important questions.

Conclusion

The test-taking strategies you have learned in this chapter will let you do your best on the TAKS. By using these strategies and the information you now know about how to control test anxiety, you will be able to defeat the test monster. Use what you have learned in the first two chapters and complete the practice assessments in the rest of this book. By the end of this book, you will be ready to "show what you know" on the TAKS for Grade 5.

Science

Introduction

In the Science section of the Texas Assessment of Knowledge and Skills (TAKS), you will be asked questions to test what you have learned so far in school. These questions are based on the science skills you have been taught in school through fifth grade. The questions you will answer are not meant to confuse or trick you but are written so you have the best chance to show what you know.

Questions I Will Answer on the TAKS

There are two types of questions on the Science TAKS for Grade 5: multiple-choice items and griddable items. Some questions are based on information, such as a paragraph, a table, or an illustration. Make sure you look over everything carefully before answering a question.

Multiple-choice items have four answer choices, and only one is correct. An example of a multiple-choice item is shown below.

For a griddable item, you mark your answer using numbers. An example of a griddable item is shown below. You write your answer in the boxes at the top of the grid; then, you darken the bubbles to mark the correct number. In the example given, a student has recorded an answer of "580." The numbers are written at the top of the grid, and the bubble for each number is marked below. A decimal point is shown in the last column to help you understand the place value of the numbers you record. If you're not sure how to mark your answer for a griddable item, ask a parent or a teacher to show you.

Multiple-Choice Question

1   Tiara looks up at the sky one night. She sees a constellation of stars. Four weeks later, Tiara looks up at the sky. She looks at the same spot she looked at the previous month. The constellation is not in the same spot. What causes this?

   ○ A   The stars in the constellation revolve around the Earth.

   ● B   The Earth revolves around the Sun.

   ○ C   The Earth revolves around the moon.

   ○ D   The stars in the constellation revolve around the Sun.

Griddable Item

2   Based on the information in the table below, how many minutes of sunlight were there on Monday?

Day	Sunrise	Sunset	Minutes
Sunday	7:20	4:59	579
Monday	7:20	5:00	?
Tuesday	7:21	5:00	581

Record and bubble in your answer on the answer document.

5	8	0	.
⓪	⓪	●	
①	①	①	
②	②	②	
③	③	③	
④	④	④	
●	⑤	⑤	
⑥	⑥	⑥	
⑦	⑦	⑦	
⑧	●	⑧	
⑨	⑨	⑨	

Directions for Assessment 1

Assessment 1 is made up of multiple-choice questions and griddable items. For a multiple-choice question, fill in one answer bubble to mark the correct answer. For a griddable item, write your answer in the boxes. Then, fill in the bubbles. Be sure to use the correct place value.

Read each question carefully. If you do not know an answer, you may skip the question and come back to it later.

You will not be permitted to use calculators on this section of the test.

When you finish, check your answers.

Use the information below and your knowledge of science to help you answer questions 1-3.

Members of Mr. Kish's science class are going to do an experiment. They will be working with liquids. First, Mr. Kish talks about the safety rules for working with liquids. Then, Mr. Kish passes out a set of directions for all the students.

Andre is one of Mr. Kish's new students. He has never worked in a science lab. This experiment will be his first. Mr. Kish suggests that Andre and Maria work as a team because Maria has worked in the lab many times. Mr. Kish instructs the students to begin. Andre jumps from his seat, but he is the only one. He starts setting materials, including beakers and tubes, on the lab counter. The other students are busy reading the instructions.

1   What safety procedure does Andre not follow?

   A Andre does not want to follow the rules for working with liquids.

   B Andre does not select the correct materials.

   C Andre does not read the instructions before starting work in the lab.

   D Andre does not listen to Maria's instructions.

2   While working on the experiment, Maria and Andre spill some liquid. What is the first thing Maria and Andre should do?

   A They should tell their friends about the accident.

   B They should tell their teacher about the accident.

   C They should pretend nothing happened.

   D They should continue the experiment.

3   What safety equipment should all the students wear for this experiment, which involves liquids?

   A helmets

   B safety goggles

   C boots

   D fireproof gloves

4 Which of the following is considered a testable hypothesis?

- **A** Water slightly erodes loose topsoil.
- **B** Seeds will grow without light.
- **C** Trees grow in good soil.
- **D** Animals will grow if they are happy.

5 Allen makes the prediction that it will rain 4 days next week. What information must Allen gather to test his prediction?

- **A** the amount of rainfall each day next week
- **B** the amount of rainfall each day this week
- **C** the amount of rainfall each day for the same week last year
- **D** the amount of rainfall each day for this month

6 Four steps of the scientific method are listed below. During which step would a scientist analyze information from an experiment?

> Step 1: State the Problem
>
> Step 2: Form a Hypothesis
>
> Step 3: Test the Hypothesis
>
> Step 4: Draw a Conclusion

- **A** Step 1
- **B** Step 2
- **C** Step 3
- **D** Step 4

7 During one experiment, Jane found that it takes 12 seconds for a pinwheel to stop spinning. Which of the following is a valid conclusion?

- **A** Friction caused the pinwheel to spin.
- **B** All pinwheels will stop spinning after 12 seconds.
- **C** The pinwheel begins to spin when a force acts upon it.
- **D** All less expensive pinwheels will spin for less than 12 seconds.

Day	Plant's Height
Day 1	3 centimeters
Day 8	2 centimeters
Day 15	6 centimeters
Day 21	10 centimeters

8 Kylie's plant grows a little each week. Kylie created the chart above to show her results. What mistake did Kylie make?

- **A** She stopped measuring the plant's height at Day 21.
- **B** She should have measured the plant using inches.
- **C** She did not measure the plant every day.
- **D** She measured incorrectly on Day 8.

GO ON ▶

Use the information below and your knowledge of science to help you answer questions 9-11.

George wanted to determine whether a battery's cost affects how long it lasts. George bought four packs of batteries. All the batteries were the same size, but they were different brands. The brands George bought are listed from the least expensive to the most expensive: Brand A, Brand B, Brand C, and Brand D. George predicted that Brand D battery would last the longest. It was the most expensive.

George gathered together wires, a stopwatch, four of the same kind of light bulbs, and graph paper. George tested the four different brands of batteries by hooking up each of the batteries to a separate light bulb using wire. He then used his stopwatch to keep track of the length of time each bulb stayed lit. It took several days to gather his data.

After the experiment, George recorded his results. The Brand D battery lasted the longest, 10 hours and 20 minutes. The Brand C battery came in second place; it lasted 9 hours and 17 minutes. Brand B was third; it lasted 7 hours and 30 minutes. Brand A only lasted for 5 hours and 58 minutes. George discovered that cost does relate to how long a battery lasts.

9   What was George's hypothesis?

   A   More expensive batteries will last longer than less expensive batteries.

   B   Less expensive batteries will last longer than more expensive batteries.

   C   All the batteries will last the same amount of time.

   D   Brand B batteries will outlast all the other batteries.

10   Based on George's experiment, one might infer that –

   A   the more expensive a battery is, the longer it will last

   B   the more expensive a battery is, the shorter it will last

   C   the more expensive a battery is, the more batteries you will need

   D   the less expensive a battery is, the longer it will last

11 Based on what you know about George's experiment, what is wrong with this model?

○ **A** The light bulbs should all be different sizes.

○ **B** The batteries should be different sizes.

○ **C** The light bulbs should all be the same size.

○ **D** The batteries should all be the same brand.

12   Chantell is measuring how long it takes for a container of water to boil. When the experiment finishes, Chantell stops the timing device. It reads 4:50. She learns that it took 4 minutes and 50 seconds for the container of water to boil. What did Chantell's stopwatch look like before the experiment began?

   A Stopwatch A

   B Stopwatch B

   C Stopwatch C

   D Stopwatch D

13   Which of the following is true about a compass?

   A A compass contains a magnet that has a north pole pointing to the magnetic north.

   B A compass contains a barometer that has a north pole pointing to the magnetic north.

   C A compass contains a battery that has a south pole pointing to the magnetic south.

   D A compass contains a thermometer that has a north pole pointing to the magnetic north.

14 Zebras are known for their stripes. When do zebras inherit this trait from their parents?

⬭ **A** when they are born

⬭ **B** before they are born

⬭ **C** when they die

⬭ **D** between birth and age one

15 Kara went to the pet store. She bought a parrot. When she brought the parrot home, she put it in a special bird cage. What behavior might the new parrot learn?

⬭ **A** how to eat food

⬭ **B** how to say a few words

⬭ **C** how to drink water

⬭ **D** how to build a nest

16 What determines a person's natural eye color?

⬭ **A** only the mother's eye color

⬭ **B** DNA

⬭ **C** only the father's eye color

⬭ **D** dye

GO ON

17 An eagle has sharp, curved talons. What does this characteristic most likely tell you about eagles?

    A Eagles use their talons to help them swim.

    B Eagles use their talons to transport their young.

    C Eagles use their talons to gather seeds.

    D Eagles use their talons to catch their prey.

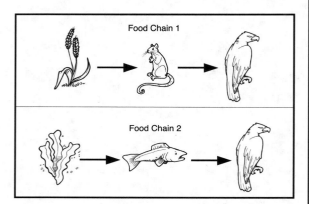

Food Chain 1

Food Chain 2

18 The arrows on the food chain shown above point to –

    A the organism that is a predator

    B the organism that releases energy

    C the organism that is a carnivore

    D the organism that takes in energy

19 A rabbit depends on vegetation for food. A rabbit is a –

    A first level predator

    B first level producer

    C first level consumer

    D second level consumer

20 A housing development has cut down half of the trees in a forest. What must the organisms that live in the forest do in order to survive?

    A The organisms must compete with one another for the limited resources that are left in the habitat.

    B The organisms must learn to get along with the people who will move into the houses.

    C The organisms must stop having offspring in order to limit the strain on the resources.

    D The organisms must migrate to another area that offers fewer resources.

Butterfly Cycle

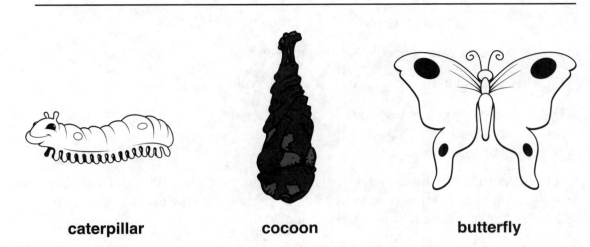

caterpillar   cocoon   butterfly

21 Look at the pictures of the butterfly cycle. What stage is missing?

⬭ **A** adult

⬭ **B** pupa

⬭ **C** larva

⬭ **D** egg

22 A beehive and a flower bed are both present in Karl's backyard. If the beehive is destroyed, how will the flowers be affected?

⬭ **A** The flowers may have fewer resources.

⬭ **B** The flowers may grow larger because there is more room.

⬭ **C** The flowers may not be pollinated.

⬭ **D** The flowers may not have to compete for resources.

GO ON

23 During the winter months, the temperature begins to drop in North America. During this time, bears hibernate. Why do bears hibernate?

    ⬭ **A** They need the sleep in order to hunt during the spring.

    ⬭ **B** Their bodies cannot handle the cold temperatures.

    ⬭ **C** They need to use the excess energy stored by their bodies.

    ⬭ **D** Their food supply is very low.

24 In parts of the northwest United States, logging is destroying many forests. These forests are home to the spotted owl. Many people worry that logging will result in the extinction of the spotted owl. What is the main cause of extinction?

    ⬭ **A** fishing

    ⬭ **B** hunting

    ⬭ **C** global warming

    ⬭ **D** loss of habitat

25 Which behavior represents an organism changing its environment to meet its needs?

    ⬭ **A** a bird building a nest

    ⬭ **B** a bird drinking from a puddle

    ⬭ **C** a bird eating berries on a bush

    ⬭ **D** a bird resting on a tree branch

26 Which of the following is true?

    ⬭ **A** Consumers are a food source for producers.

    ⬭ **B** Producers are a food source for consumers.

    ⬭ **C** Producers are not a food source.

    ⬭ **D** Consumers are not a food source.

GO ON

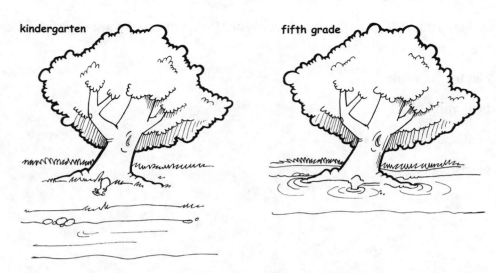

kindergarten   fifth grade

27 When Joaquin was in kindergarten, an oak tree grew on the other side of the creek. When Joaquin was in fifth grade, he saw that the oak tree was in the path of the creek's flow. What most likely caused this change?

   ⬭ A The tree moved itself into the creek in order to get more water.

   ⬭ B The flow of the creek changed its course.

   ⬭ C Someone dug up the tree and replanted it in the creek.

   ⬭ D A new oak tree grew out of the creek, and the original tree died.

28 In an ecosystem, when an animal dies, its remains are broken down by –

   ⬭ A animals

   ⬭ B consumers

   ⬭ C decomposers

   ⬭ D plants

29 What is one way seasonal changes affect organisms?

   ⬭ A The supply of resources does not change.

   ⬭ B The supply of resources is always changing.

   ⬭ C The supply of resources is always restricted.

   ⬭ D The supply of resources is always increasing.

GO ON

30 Kya's mom burns some logs in the fireplace. What forms of energy are released by the burning logs?

⬭ **A** electric and solar

⬭ **B** heat and light

⬭ **C** heat and mechanical

⬭ **D** electric and light

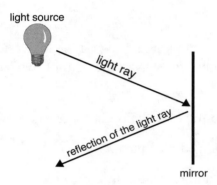

31 What does the diagram of the light ray and its reflection show you?

⬭ **A** Light that hits a reflective surface and forms a right angle with the surface reflects at an angle.

⬭ **B** Light that hits a reflective surface at an angle reflects back along the same path as the light ray.

⬭ **C** Light that hits a reflective surface at an angle reflects at the same angle but in the opposite direction.

⬭ **D** Light that hits a reflective surface at an angle scatters.

32 A 9-volt battery has two posts on top. One post is marked with a plus sign (+). The other post is marked with a negative sign (−). Which of the following is true?

○ **A** Electrons flow into both posts but never flow out of either post.

○ **B** Electrons flow out of both posts but never flow into either post.

○ **C** Electrons don't flow into or out of either post, but protons do.

○ **D** Electrons flow into one post and flow out of the other post.

33 Sound energy can travel through things that vibrate. Sound energy cannot travel through −

○ **A** water

○ **B** air

○ **C** a vacuum

○ **D** solids

GO ON ▶

Use the information below and your knowledge of science to help you answer questions 34-37.

Dominick has several breakfast options. He can have a bowl of cereal with milk. He can have a piece of bread that has been toasted and is topped with butter. He can have a hard-boiled egg, or he can have a scrambled egg.

Dominick decides he would like to have a piece of toast and a bowl of cereal. He puts the bread in the toaster. While the bread is toasting, he fills his bowl with milk and cereal. The cereal is made of big wheat flakes. Dominick returns to the toaster. When the bread pops up, it is toasted. He puts his hand on the outside of the toaster; the outside of the toaster feels hot. Dominick cuts a pat from the stick of butter. When the butter hits the bread, it begins to melt.

34 What is true about the toaster?

   A The material on the outside of the toaster is magnetic.

   B The material on the outside of the toaster is a source of electricity.

   C The material on the outside of the toaster is a conductor of heat.

   D The material on the outside of the toaster is an insulator.

35 What is true about Dominick's milk and cereal?

   A The mixture of milk and cereal cannot be separated.

   B The mixture includes two solids.

   C The mixture includes a liquid and a solid.

   D The mixture forms a new substance.

36 What is true about Dominick's toast?

   A Bread becoming toast is an example of a chemical change.

   B Bread becoming toast is an example of a physical change.

   C Toast becoming bread is an example of a physical change.

   D Toast becoming bread is an example of a chemical change.

37 What is true about the temperature of Dominick's toast?

   A The temperature of the toast was lower than the melting point of butter.

   B The temperature of the toast was at the melting point of butter or higher.

   C The temperature of the toast was at the boiling point of butter or higher.

   D The temperature of the toast was at the same temperature as the butter.

GO ON ▶

38 What causes the piano to move up the ramp?

⬭ **A** force is applied by the boy

⬭ **B** gravity pushes the piano up the ramp

⬭ **C** the ramp pulls the piano up

⬭ **D** inertia causes the piano to stay in motion

39 Which of the following would reduce the effort required to push the piano up the ramp?

⬭ **A** the height of the ramp is decreased

⬭ **B** the height of the ramp is increased

⬭ **C** the weight of the piano is increased

⬭ **D** the weight of the ramp is reduced

GO ON ▶

40   A lamp is an example of a circuit. When the lamp switch is on, the light bulb lights up. When the lamp switch is off, there is no light. Which of the following is true?

    ◯ **A** When the lamp switch is on, the circuit is closed.

    ◯ **B** When the lamp switch is off, the circuit is closed.

    ◯ **C** When the lamp switch is on, the circuit is open.

    ◯ **D** When the lamp switch is off, the circuit is complete.

41   The movement of electrons produces what type of energy?

    ◯ **A** solar

    ◯ **B** electrical

    ◯ **C** nutritional

    ◯ **D** microscopic

42 Weathering is caused by –

⬭ **A** sedimentary rock

⬭ **B** wind, water, and plants

⬭ **C** consumers

⬭ **D** decomposers

43 When compared to the Earth, the moon is –

⬭ **A** arid

⬭ **B** larger

⬭ **C** the same size

⬭ **D** more populated

44 Which of the following is not true about glaciers?

⬭ **A** Glaciers can create cliffs by cutting into earth.

⬭ **B** Glaciers can create rivers by carving a path in the soil.

⬭ **C** Glaciers can create valleys by removing soil.

⬭ **D** Glaciers can create forests by removing soil.

45   Which of the following is an example of erosion?

　　　　A   Roots hold soil in place.

　　　　B   Rain washes away a sand dune.

　　　　C   A glacier deposits soil in a low-lying area.

　　　　D   Decaying matter returns nutrients to the soil.

The Contour Map of the Earth's Layers

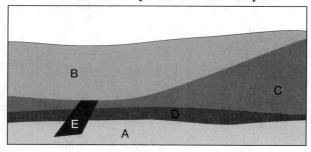

46   The contour map above shows several layers of the Earth. What most likely caused Layer E to form the way it did?

　　　　A   atmospheric gases

　　　　B   water

　　　　C   the Sun

　　　　D   sound waves

47   Tim wanted to grow some seeds. He put clay soil and a few seeds in a medium-sized pot. The pot did not have a drain hole. Tim packed the soil in the pot as tight as he could. Tim watered the seeds every day, but the plants did not grow. What is most likely the problem?

　　　　A   There are too many seeds in the pot.

　　　　B   There is not enough room for the roots to spread out.

　　　　C   The soil does not have enough nutrients.

　　　　D   The water is not draining properly.

48 A mountain stands close to the ocean. The mountain is east of the ocean, and the wind is moving from west to east. In general, when compared to the opposite side, the side of the mountain that is closest to the ocean receives –

   ⬭ **A** less rainfall because most clouds move to the other side

   ⬭ **B** more rainfall because of the effects of the water vapor coming off the ocean

   ⬭ **C** the same amount of rainfall because the rate of precipitation is the same

   ⬭ **D** no rainfall because clouds move to the other side

? ⇒ plants ⇒ gazelle ⇒ lion

49 A food chain shows the flow of energy. What is missing from the food chain above?

   ⬭ **A** carbon monoxide

   ⬭ **B** photosynthesis

   ⬭ **C** the Sun

   ⬭ **D** fertilizer

50 Kyle's dad wants to use an inexhaustible resource to heat his home. What energy source could he use?

   ⬭ **A** solar power

   ⬭ **B** a fossil fuel

   ⬭ **C** wood

   ⬭ **D** electricity

51 Which of the following correctly lists the planets in relation to the Sun?

   ⬭ **A** Earth, Jupiter, Mars, Mercury, Neptune, Pluto, Saturn, the Sun, Uranus, Venus,

   ⬭ **B** Mercury, Venus, Earth, Mars, Jupiter, Saturn, Uranus, Neptune, Pluto, the Sun

   ⬭ **C** The Sun, Mercury, Venus, Earth, Mars, Jupiter, Saturn, Uranus, Neptune, Pluto

   ⬭ **D** The Sun, Mars, Venus, Earth, Mercury, Jupiter, Saturn, Uranus, Neptune, Pluto

52 Because oil, natural gas, and coal were formed millions of years ago from the remains of plants and animals, they are called –

   ⬭ **A** animal fuels

   ⬭ **B** organic fuels

   ⬭ **C** fossil fuels

   ⬭ **D** geothermal fuels

GO ON ▶

53 When the Earth is between the moon and the Sun –

⬭ **A** the moon is full because the entire lighted half can be seen

⬭ **B** the moon is new because the moon cannot reflect the Sun's light

⬭ **C** the moon is full because the Earth casts a shadow on the moon

⬭ **D** the moon is partially lit because some of the Sun's light is reflected

54 What is true about the gas exhaled by animals and the gas taken in by plants?

⬭ **A** Animals exhale oxygen, and plants take in oxygen.

⬭ **B** Animals exhale carbon dioxide, and plants take in carbon dioxide.

⬭ **C** Animals exhale oxygen, and plants take in carbon dioxide.

⬭ **D** Animals exhale carbon dioxide, and plants take in oxygen.

55 The moon completely orbits the Earth about once a –

- **A** day
- **B** week
- **C** month
- **D** year

56 Day and night are caused by –

- **A** the moon as it orbits the Earth
- **B** the Sun as it orbits the Earth
- **C** the Earth as it rotates on its axis
- **D** the Earth as it orbits the Sun

Directions for Assessment 2

Assessment 2 is made up of multiple-choice questions and griddable items. For a multiple-choice question, fill in one answer bubble to mark the correct answer. For a griddable item, write your answer in the boxes. Then, fill in the bubbles. Be sure to use the correct place value.

Read each question carefully. If you do not know an answer, you may skip the question and come back to it later.

You will not be permitted to use calculators on this section of the test.

When you finish, check your answers.

1   Joanne's class performs an experiment in the school lab. She tries to create the experiment at home. The experiment does not work. She wants to ask someone what she did wrong, but there is no one at home. What do you know is true about Joanne's experiment?

   A   Joanne left the directions at school, and that is why her experiment did not work.

   B   Joanne broke a safety rule because she performed an experiment without supervision.

   C   Joanne's experiment did not work because she performed it without help.

   D   Joanne's experiment did not work because she did not perform it in the school lab.

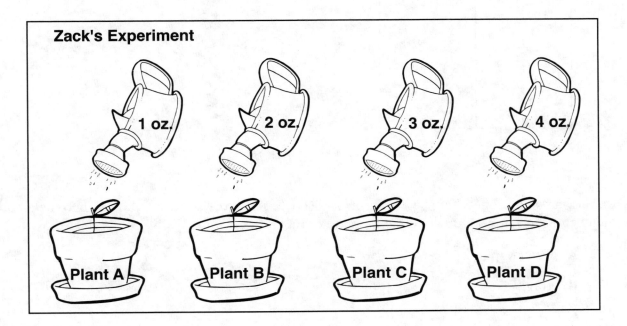

2   The picture above shows Zack's experiment. He plans to water his plants every other day. Zack's experiment most likely tests the hypothesis that –

   A   the size of the pot affects how much water the plant needs

   B   the amount of water given to a plant will affect its growth

   C   different plants need different amounts of water

   D   different plants need different types of water

GO ON ➡

3 The thermometer shows the temperature in the school cafeteria in degrees Fahrenheit. What is the temperature? Record and bubble in your answer on the answer document.

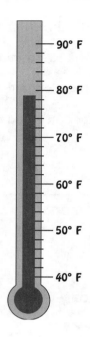

4 Maria wants to test how far she can throw a baseball. She throws the ball. It rises into the air and then begins to fall back down to the ground. Maria knows that the ball's drop is caused by –

   A water vapor

   B gravity

   C wind

   D magnetism

GO ON

5   Tara rolls a ball along the ground. Each time she rolls it, the ball goes farther than it did before. Which graph shows the results of Tara's experiment?

◯ **A**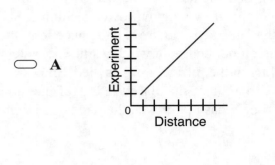

◯ **C**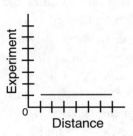

◯ **B**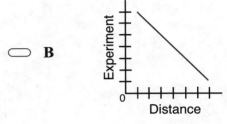

◯ **D**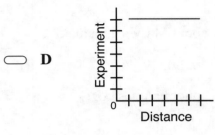

6   Jean is in fifth grade. Jean predicts that all the students in his fifth-grade class will be 68 inches tall by the age of 21. Jean must support his prediction at the fifth-grade science fair. What is true about Jean's prediction?

◯ **A** it cannot be tested

◯ **B** it can never be proven true

◯ **C** it can be supported with indirect evidence

◯ **D** it can be proven true with statistics about the average height of human beings

GO ON ▶

Use the information below and your knowledge of science to help you answer questions 7-8.

Mary is going to enter the fifth-grade science fair. She decides that she will perform an experiment to test whether a lack of sunlight will affect the growth of sunflower seedlings. She plants two sunflowers in two separate pots. After both plants begin to grow, she puts one in the refrigerator. She places the other one in direct sunlight on her bedroom windowsill. She waters each plant daily. After a week, she sees that the seedling in the refrigerator has died. She concludes that the lack of sunlight killed the sunflower plant that she placed in the refrigerator. The judge at the science fair tells Mary that her experiment has not proven that lack of sunlight killed the sunflower plant.

7   What is true about Mary's conclusion?

    A It is valid.

    B It cannot be retested.

    C It is invalid.

    D It is acceptable.

8   What mistake did Mary make?

    A She did not control all of her variables.

    B She left the plant in the refrigerator too long.

    C She forgot to water both plants.

    D She should have used fertilizer on one of the plants.

9   The drawing above shows a model of the Sun, the Earth, and the moon. What is wrong with this model?

    A The Earth should be smaller than the Sun and the moon.

    B The Sun should be larger than the Earth and the moon.

    C The moon should be larger than the Earth.

    D The Earth should be smaller than the moon but larger than the Sun.

10   Carrie wants to see what exists in a drop of water. Which instrument should she use?

    ◯ **A**   a hand lens

    ◯ **B**   binoculars

    ◯ **C**   a microscope

    ◯ **D**   a balance

11   Trent buys a tube of Glow White toothpaste. The box says, "Ninety percent of dentists surveyed use Glow White." What does this mean?

    ◯ **A**   Ninety percent of all people who responded to the survey use Glow White.

    ◯ **B**   Of those people who were asked, ninety percent said they use Glow White.

    ◯ **C**   Ninety percent of all dentists were surveyed.

    ◯ **D**   Of those dentists who were asked, ninety percent said they use Glow White.

12   Dillon held a rubber ball out the window. There was a sidewalk below the window. Dillon made this statement. "When I let go of the ball, it will fall down to the sidewalk." Dillon's statement can be described as –

    ◯ **A**   a prediction

    ◯ **B**   a conclusion

    ◯ **C**   an observation

    ◯ **D**   a fabrication

13   Sergio had to make up a test during his lunch period, so he brought a sack lunch to the science lab. While his partner starts an experiment, Sergio eats a sandwich. Which of the following is true?

    ◯ **A**   Sergio should eat his lunch during the experiment so he is not hungry.

    ◯ **B**   Sergio should wait to eat until the experiment is halfway complete.

    ◯ **C**   Sergio should share his lunch with his partner.

    ◯ **D**   Sergio should not eat while working in the lab.

GO ON ➤

14 Tisha is blind. She is led around by her guide dog, a golden retriever named Max. Max has the ability to lead Tisha down hallways, to let Tisha know when she is at the top of a stairwell, and to push the button for the elevator. Max's abilities –

○ **A** are inherited from his parents

○ **B** are inherited from Tisha

○ **C** are learned behaviors

○ **D** are genetic traits

15 Which of the following improves a bird's ability to survive?

○ **A** They build their nests on the ground where they are easily seen.

○ **B** They limit the number of offspring they produce.

○ **C** They never leave their nests in order to protect their habitat.

○ **D** They migrate to warmer climates when necessary.

16 Lions are predators. They feast on many different types of prey, such as giraffes, gazelles, and wildebeests. What characteristic must these predators have?

○ **A** the ability to climb trees

○ **B** the ability to hunt

○ **C** the ability to use weapons

○ **D** the ability to swim

17 Forests are being cut down for timber. Many people believe new trees should be planted in these areas after the old trees are removed. Which of the following does not support this belief?

○ **A** The new trees prevent erosion.

○ **B** The new trees provide oxygen.

○ **C** The new trees exhaust the soil's supply of nutrients.

○ **D** The new trees will provide a habitat for organisms.

GO ON

18   Read this information about a food chain. A fish eats a tadpole, and then an eagle eats the fish. What is missing?

⬭ **A** what type of eagle ate the fish

⬭ **B** what ate the fish

⬭ **C** what the tadpole ate

⬭ **D** what time of day this happened

19   Which of the following is not true?

⬭ **A** Both plants and animals need water.

⬭ **B** Both plants and animals need oxygen.

⬭ **C** Both plants and animals need food.

⬭ **D** Both plants and animals need a way to dispose of waste.

20   Why do plants have leaves?

⬭ **A** to capture energy from the Sun

⬭ **B** to change colors in the fall

⬭ **C** to capture oxygen

⬭ **D** to produce carbon dioxide

21   Plants that survive in the desert are exposed to harsh conditions. Deserts are very dry and very hot. Desert plants must adapt to their environment. They must have –

⬭ **A** the ability to reproduce without water

⬭ **B** the ability to migrate

⬭ **C** the ability to collect and store water

⬭ **D** the ability to live without any water

22 In a tundra ecosystem, the temperature rises above 32º F less than 60 days a year. In a deciduous forest ecosystem, the average temperature is 50º F. What can you conclude about the life cycle of a tundra plant?

⬭ **A** It is more varied than a plant's life cycle in the deciduous forest.

⬭ **B** It is equal to a plant's life cycle in the deciduous forest.

⬭ **C** It is longer than a plant's life cycle in the deciduous forest.

⬭ **D** It is shorter than a plant's life cycle in the deciduous forest.

23 Which of these is an example of matter in a solid state?

⬭ **A** dirt

⬭ **B** steam

⬭ **C** water

⬭ **D** air

24 A force in the same direction as motion will affect speed by –

⬭ **A** decreasing it

⬭ **B** not changing it

⬭ **C** increasing it

⬭ **D** completely stopping it

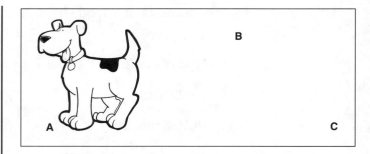

25 The dog barks while standing at point A. The bark is louder at point B than at point C –

⬭ **A** because sound waves are more condensed at point B

⬭ **B** because sound waves cannot travel as far as point C

⬭ **C** because sound waves are more condensed at point C

⬭ **D** because sound waves only travel in one direction

26 Katherine buys a salt lick for deer. A salt lick is a cube of salt. She puts the salt lick in her backyard. She hopes to watch the deer come to the salt lick. Katherine watches the cube for many weeks, but she never sees any deer. She thinks the rainy days are keeping them away. Even though the deer have not been licking the salt cube, Katherine notices its size is getting smaller. Which of the following is true?

⬭ **A** The Sun causes particles of the salt lick to disappear.

⬭ **B** The rain causes particles of the salt lick to break off and dissolve.

⬭ **C** The Sun causes particles of the salt lick to dissolve.

⬭ **D** The rain cause particles of the salt lick to disappear.

GO ON ▶

27 How is solar energy different from electrical energy?

○ A Electrical energy is created by the Sun; solar energy is not.

○ B Solar energy is an inexhaustible resource; electrical energy is not.

○ C Solar energy is caused by a chemical reaction; electrical energy is not.

○ D Electrical energy is an inexhaustible resource; solar energy is not.

28 Which of the following can block the flow of a current through a circuit?

○ A a conductor

○ B an insulator

○ C a piece of metal

○ D a wire

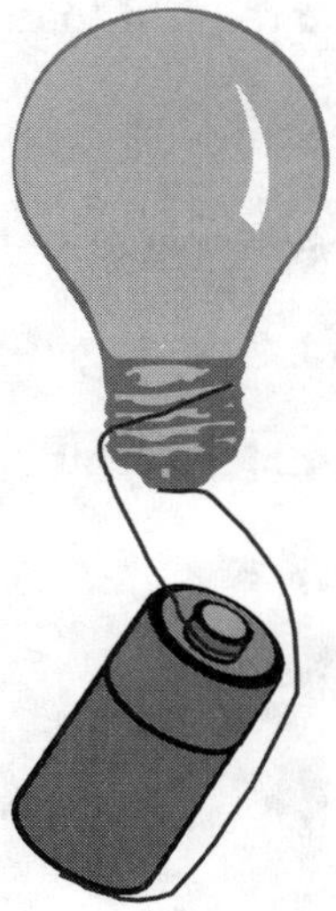

29 In this experiment, a light bulb is connected to a battery using wires. When all the connections are made between the battery and the bulb, the bulb lights. It takes energy to light the bulb. Where does this energy come from?

○ A It is stored in the glass of the light bulb.

○ B It is stored in the battery.

○ C It is stored in the wire.

○ D It is stored in the metal base of the light bulb.

30 Which of the following is an example of combustion?

○ A mixing water and salt

○ B crashing a car

○ C sawing a log in half

○ D burning a candle

GO ON

31 Which words are used to describe the physical states of matter?

⬭ **A** reflective, refractive, magnetic

⬭ **B** dense, loose, tight

⬭ **C** solid, liquid, gas

⬭ **D** chemical, electrical, solar

The Contour Map of the Earth's Layers

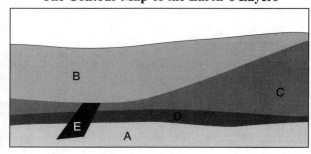

32 Which layer on the contour map shown above is oldest?

⬭ **A** Layer B

⬭ **B** Layer D

⬭ **C** Layer E

⬭ **D** Layer A

33 Scientists look at tree rings to determine how old a tree is. For each year of a tree's life, it adds a layer (a ring) to its trunk and branches. Rings are thicker when resources are plentiful. Rings are thinner when resources are scarce. Which of the following will cause a tree to add a thick ring?

⬭ **A** pollution

⬭ **B** temperatures that are colder than normal

⬭ **C** a large amount of rainfall

⬭ **D** a drought

Phases of the Moon

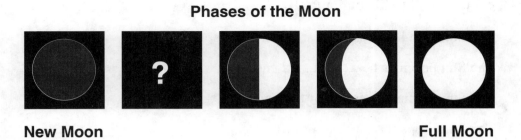

New Moon   **Full Moon**

34   What phase of the moon is missing in the diagram?

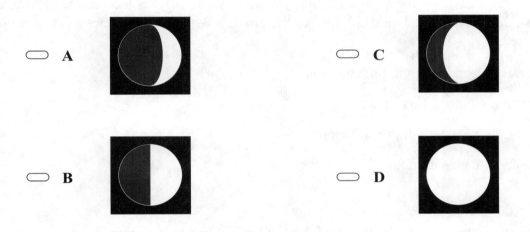

A   C

B   D

35   In a marine ecosystem, what causes waves?

⬭ **A** a cycle of gravity pushing water up and wind pushing it down

⬭ **B** a cycle of underwater forces pushing water down and gravity pushing it up

⬭ **C** a cycle of underwater forces pushing water up and wind pushing it down

⬭ **D** a cycle of wind pushing water up and gravity pushing it down

36   According to Alisa, fossil fuels are formed from the remains of dead plants and animals. Alisa says we can easily create more fossil fuels. Alisa tells a friend that fossil fuels are inexhaustible resources. Is this true?

⬭ **A** No, it takes millions of years for fossil fuels to develop.

⬭ **B** Yes, we will never run out of dead plants and animals.

⬭ **C** No, fossil fuels are renewable resources because we can generate more.

⬭ **D** Yes, there is an endless supply of fossil fuels below the Earth's surface.

37 Why is the Sun central to life on Earth?

⬭ **A** The Sun is in between the Earth and the moon.

⬭ **B** The Sun provides heat, light, and energy.

⬭ **C** The Sun warms the center of the Earth.

⬭ **D** The Sun keeps the Earth in orbit.

38 During the water cycle, water that is stored on Earth turns from a liquid to a gas known as water vapor. The water vapor cools to form clouds. When the water vapor reaches a certain temperature, the water vapor turns back into a liquid and falls to the ground. What are the names of the stages in the water cycle?

⬭ **A** evaporation, condensation, precipitation

⬭ **B** vaporizing, condensation, rain

⬭ **C** evaporation, conduction, precipitation

⬭ **D** evaporation, concentration, rain

39 When a hemisphere of the Earth is tilted away from the Sun, in that hemisphere, it is –

⬭ **A** fall

⬭ **B** winter

⬭ **C** spring

⬭ **D** summer

40 A warm ocean current causes the nearby climate to be –

⬭ **A** warm

⬭ **B** unstable

⬭ **C** cool

⬭ **D** dry

Reading

Introduction

In the Reading section of the Texas Assessment of Knowledge and Skills (TAKS), you will be asked questions to test what you have learned so far in school. These questions are based on the reading skills you have been taught in school through fifth grade. The questions you will answer are not meant to confuse or trick you but are written so you have the best chance to show what you know.

Questions I Will Answer on the TAKS

You will answer multiple-choice questions on the Reading TAKS for Grade 5. Multiple-choice items have four answer choices, and only one is correct.

The questions are based on reading selections. The selections may be narrative or expository. Narrative selections are fiction. Expository selections are informative. There may also be selections with more than one part. Make sure you read all the texts carefully.

Examples of an expository selection and a multiple-choice item are shown below.

Hummingbirds

1   Have you ever heard the humming sound of the hummingbird? These tiny birds get their name from the sound they make when their wings beat rapidly in the air. Your chances of catching a long gaze of one are not good, however. Hummingbirds don't hang around in one spot for very long.

2   Hummingbirds feed on nectar. Nectar is a sweet substance found in flowers. You might see these flowers in your garden or in the backyard. Hummingbirds are attracted to bright red- and orange-colored blooms more than to other colors. To get to the nectar, hummingbirds reach their lengthy tongues down into the flowers. Nectar isn't the only thing that the hummingbird likes to eat. It will also eat tiny insects that hide out in the flowers.

3   One unusual feature of the hummingbird is that it can fly backwards. This comes in handy when the bird flies toward and away from flowers as it gathers nectar. It is the only bird with this unique gift.

4   There are about two dozen types of hummingbirds in the United States. The ruby-throated hummingbird is the most common. It can be found throughout the South. It is about four inches long and is easy to spot. Male ruby throats are shiny green in color. They have brilliant red throats and white breasts. The female is less brightly colored. It does not have a ruby throat.

1   Based on the passage, what is unusual about a hummingbird?

⬭   **A**   It can fly.

⬭   **B**   It lives in the United States.

⬛   **C**   It can fly backwards.

⬭   **D**   It is about four inches long.

Directions for Assessment 1

Assessment 1 is made up of multiple-choice questions. For a multiple-choice question, fill in one answer bubble to mark the correct answer.

Read each selection and each question carefully. If you do not know an answer, you may skip the question and come back to it later.

When you finish, check your answers.

Hummingbirds

1   Have you ever heard the humming sound of the hummingbird? These tiny birds get their name from the sound they make when their wings beat <u>rapidly</u> in the air. Your chances of catching a long <u>gaze</u> of one are not good, however. Hummingbirds don't hang around in one spot for very long.

2   Hummingbirds feed on nectar. Nectar is a sweet substance found in flowers. You might see these flowers in your garden or in the backyard. Hummingbirds are attracted to bright red- and orange-colored blooms more than to other colors. To get to the nectar, hummingbirds reach their <u>lengthy</u> tongues down into the flowers. Nectar isn't the only thing that the hummingbird likes to eat. It will also eat tiny insects that hide out in the flowers.

3   One unusual feature of the hummingbird is that it can fly backwards. This comes in handy when the bird flies toward and away from flowers as it gathers nectar. It is the only bird with this unique gift.

4   There are about two dozen types of hummingbirds in the United States. The ruby-throated hummingbird is the most common. It can be found throughout the South. It is about four inches long and is easy to spot. Male ruby throats are shiny green in color. They have <u>brilliant</u> red throats and white breasts. The female is less brightly colored. It does not have a ruby throat.

1   Read this sentence from paragraph 1.

> *Your chances of catching a long <u>gaze</u> of one are not good, however.*

What does <u>gaze</u> mean?

⬭ **A** look

⬭ **B** sound

⬭ **C** movement

⬭ **D** flight

2   Read the meanings below for the word <u>brilliant</u>.

> **bril•liant** (bril´yənt) *adjective*
> **1.** full of light **2.** sharp and
> clear like a sound **3.** rich in
> color **4.** highly intelligent

Which meaning best fits the way <u>brilliant</u> is used in paragraph 4?

- **A** Meaning 1
- **B** Meaning 2
- **C** Meaning 3
- **D** Meaning 4

3   What does <u>rapidly</u> mean in paragraph 1?

- **A** with a quiet sound
- **B** in a slow manner
- **C** without moving
- **D** in a fast manner

4   Read this sentence from paragraph 2.

> *To get to the nectar, hummingbirds reach their <u>lengthy</u> tongues down into the flowers.*

What does <u>lengthy</u> mean?

- **A** long
- **B** hard to move
- **C** wide
- **D** strong

Tucker the Squirrel

1   The afternoon sky turned a deep blue. The wind began to blow. It broke off the smallest limbs of the oak trees in Jonathan's backyard. Even though it was late May, Jonathan heard on the radio that a spell of cool weather was on its way. The days hadn't become too hot yet, but he thought the crisp, fresh air felt nice just the same.

2   At the dinner table, Jonathan and his family talked about the change in weather. They discussed plans for a trip to the lake. He picked at his green peas and daydreamed about summer, friends, and no school. After finishing dinner, Jonathan and his little sister cleaned up the kitchen and put away the dishes.

3   Out the window, Jonathan could see Rudy, his dog. Rudy was playing with a rubber ball. Suddenly, Rudy began to bark. He barked and barked until finally Jonathan went outside to find out what all the noise was about. When he opened the door, the wind caught it and threw it into the house with a loud SMACK! He fought the gusts and slowly pulled the door closed. Jonathan made his way down the porch steps. He saw Rudy bumping a small animal with his nose.

4   Jonathan made his way across the green grass. His hair was swirling all around his head. Carefully, Jonathan walked toward Rudy and the tiny creature. At first, he thought it was a mouse. After a closer look, Jonathan saw that it was a baby squirrel. He looked up at the tall tree. Squirrels must have nested somewhere up there, he thought. He ran inside and called for his parents to come into the backyard.

5   Jonathan's dad lifted the baby squirrel into his hands to see if it was still alive. It had taken a long fall out of its nest, but it seemed to be OK. Jonathan and his dad recognized that it was an Eastern Gray squirrel. It looked just like the ones they had seen before in the park. Its eyes were still closed. After a little research, they guessed it was only about four weeks old.

6   They took the squirrel inside and tried to warm it up. Jonathan's mom called the wildlife department for instructions on how to help the abandoned baby. Jonathan thought it would be a great idea to raise the baby squirrel. Right away, he gave it the name "Tucker." He found a large shoebox and put an old shirt inside. Then, he put a heating pad underneath the box to help keep Tucker warm.

7   Even though Jonathan wanted to keep the squirrel as a pet, he knew that it must be released back into the wild. As soon as Tucker was old enough to find food and could survive on his own, he would be returned to the backyard. Jonathan knew that was where he really belonged.

5 What is the main idea of paragraphs 5 and 6?

   A Jonathan puts Tucker in a box to keep him warm.

   B Jonathan and his family take care of the squirrel.

   C Jonathan names the squirrel "Tucker."

   D Jonathan and his dad do research on the squirrel.

6 Why does Jonathan go outside after dinner?

   A He wants to play ball with Rudy.

   B He sees Rudy pushing something with his nose.

   C He wants to know why Rudy is barking so much.

   D He doesn't want to do the dishes.

7 Jonathan knows he can't keep Tucker because –

   A Tucker belongs in the wild once he is old enough to survive

   B Tucker is too young to find his own food

   C his parents tell him he can't have a pet

   D he doesn't know what kind of squirrel Tucker is

8 Read the first sentence of the summary below

One stormy evening, Jonathan hears his dog barking outside.

Which of the following completes the summary above?

   A Jonathan finishes his dinner and helps his family clean up the kitchen. Then, Jonathan goes outside to see why his dog is barking, and he has trouble walking because it is so windy.

   B Jonathan opens the door to go outside, and the wind blows the door shut, making a loud noise. He walks across the yard and finds a baby squirrel. He decides the squirrel must have fallen from a tree.

   C Jonathan walks across the green grass in the wind. The wind makes his hair swirl. His mom calls the wildlife department to learn about squirrels, and Jonathan's dad recognizes what kind of squirrel it is.

   D Jonathan goes outside to see why the dog is barking and finds a baby squirrel. Jonathan names the squirrel "Tucker," and he and his parents take care of the squirrel to keep it alive.

GO ON

The Stowaway

1   Polly was no ordinary penguin. As a matter of fact, she was always getting into trouble because of her sense of adventure and her overactive imagination. She and her family lived on an iceberg just north of Antarctica.

2   Every day, Polly would watch the fishing boats come and go with their nets full of fresh fish to take back to the marketplace. She loved the smell of the salty air and the sound of the fishermen talking as they did their work.

3   She knew their routine well. They moved the boats in before sunrise and then threw out the large nets until they sank into the water. After that, the fishermen rested for awhile until the nets were full of fish and other sea creatures.

4   At the sound of the captain's command, the crew lifted the nets up from the ocean and onto the deck of the fishing boat. The nets were released, and hundreds of shiny, slippery fish fell like raindrops from the sky. Polly had watched the fisherman many times and had wondered what it must be like on the boat with all those wonderful fish.

5   Sometimes, the fishermen would throw Polly a fish or two when the captain wasn't looking. This time, her curiosity was more than she could stand. Polly dove into the icy water and swam around to the other side of the boat. She found a rope ladder that had been thrown over the side. Polly made her way out of the water and onto the boat.

6   She waddled as quietly as she could all around the boat, hoping not to be caught by the fishermen. It was better than she had imagined. She saw all kinds of gadgets and wheels and more fishing nets. She also found ropes and floating rings. Polly decided that she had seen enough. Just as she was about to dive back into the water, the captain saw her. He chased Polly around the deck and almost caught her by the foot. Just as he was about to grab her, the captain slipped on a slimy piece of seaweed. Polly made her escape. She swam back to her home on the iceberg safely, but it wasn't the last time Polly's curiosity almost got her into trouble.

9   Why does Polly go aboard the fishing boat?

⬭ **A**   She needs some fish for her meal.

⬭ **B**   She is curious about what is on the boat.

⬭ **C**   The captain invited her to come aboard.

⬭ **D**   She wants to free all the captured fish.

10 The best word to describe Polly would be –

○ **A** timid

○ **B** serious

○ **C** lazy

○ **D** adventurous

11 What danger does Polly face in the story?

○ **A** Polly is chased by the captain of the fishing boat.

○ **B** Polly slips off the iceberg and can't get back up.

○ **C** Polly is hungry.

○ **D** Polly gets caught in the fishing boat's nets.

12 How would this story most likely be different if Polly did not live near the water?

○ **A** Polly would not have a good imagination.

○ **B** Polly would never go on adventures.

○ **C** Polly would not know so much about the fishing boats.

○ **D** Polly would be able to get more fish from the captain.

Alligators

1   Alligators are amazing animals. The American alligator lives in the southeast part of the United States, where the weather stays warm. Most grow to be about 10 feet long. Some of the world's biggest alligators have even grown to be 22 feet long!

2   Alligators have broad snouts that are flat and round. An alligator also has a tail, four short legs, skin that is tough and gray, and more than 70 sharp teeth. When the mouth is closed, you cannot see the bottom row of teeth. If a tooth falls out, another grows in to take its place. An alligator can live up to 75 years, and, in its lifetime, it may change teeth over 40 times! Alligators crawl around on land and swish their tails back and forth to move through the water. They cannot control the temperature of their bodies, so, if it gets too cold, they lie in the sun; if it's too hot, they float in the water.

3   Alligators are very sneaky hunters. They will stay in the water and wait for a fish, a frog, or a turtle to come too close and then, SNAP! They will even creep up on animals that have stopped for a quick drink, like birds or raccoons.

4   Like other reptiles, alligators lay their eggs on land. The mother scoops out a hole and lays as many as 50 eggs in it. She then covers the area with mud and plants and stays near the nest. About two months later, when she hears some grunting sounds, she tears the top off the nest and finds her baby alligators blinking up at her.

Crocodiles

5   Crocodiles live in the tropical and subtropical regions of the world. The American crocodile can be found mostly in Florida. Like all reptiles, crocodiles are coldblooded. This means their body temperatures depend on the environment. To stay warm, a crocodile lies in the sun.

6   The crocodile has a narrow snout. When the mouth is closed, the teeth of the lower jaw are visible. The average crocodile has about 30–40 teeth in its lower jar and has roughly the same number in its upper jaw. The jaws of crocodiles are very powerful and are extremely important for catching food.

7   These reptiles eat fish, frogs, and other small aquatic animals. Some larger crocodiles have been known to feast on deer and oxen. When searching for food, crocodiles submerge themselves in water. The eyes and nose are just above the surface as the reptile waits for a chance to catch its prey.

8   Although she spends much of her time in the water, the female crocodile lays her eggs in sand or mud. The heat of the sun helps the eggs to hatch. Similar to the female alligator, the female crocodile will protect her nest against predators looking to make a meal of her eggs.

GO ON ▶

13 Which statement tells you about how alligators hunt?

- **A** *Like other reptiles, alligators lay their eggs on land.*

- **B** *She then covers the area with mud and plants and stays near the nest.*

- **C** *They will even creep up on animals that have stopped for a quick drink, like birds or raccoons.*

- **D** *Alligators crawl around on land and swish their tails back and forth to move through the water.*

14 Because crocodiles need to stay warm, most American crocodiles are found –

- **A** in muddy places

- **B** in Florida

- **C** near other reptiles

- **D** all over the United States

15 What is one difference between paragraph 1 of "Alligators" and paragraph 1 of "Crocodiles"?

- **A** Paragraph 1 of "Alligators" tells about the length of the reptile, but paragraph 1 of "Crocodiles" does not.

- **B** Paragraph 1 of "Alligators" tells about where the reptile lives, but paragraph 1 of "Crocodiles" does not.

- **C** Paragraph 1 of "Alligators" does not tell about the length of the reptile, but paragraph 1 of "Crocodiles" does.

- **D** Paragraph 1 of "Alligators" does not tell about where the reptile lives, but paragraph 1 of "Crocodiles" does.

16 What is similar about how these two passages are organized?

- **A** Both passages explain causes and effects of trying to catch an alligator or a crocodile.

- **B** Both passages tell about the life of an alligator or a crocodile in time order.

- **C** Both passages tell a story about an alligator or a crocodile.

- **D** Both passages give facts about an alligator or a crocodile.

17 Look at the graphic below, which contains information from the passages.

- lay eggs on land
- lie in sun to keep warm
- broad snouts

Which header belongs in the empty box?

⬭ **A** Alligators and Crocodiles

⬭ **B** Crocodiles

⬭ **C** Alligators

⬭ **D** Reptiles

18 Look at the diagram below, which compares information from the passage "Alligators" and the passage "Crocodiles."

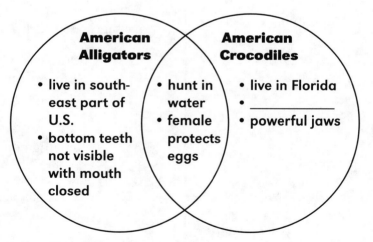

Which information belongs in the blank?

⬭ **A** bottom teeth visible with mouth closed

⬭ **B** may change teeth over 40 times

⬭ **C** no teeth visible with mouth closed

⬭ **D** will not protect eggs

68

The Gift

1   Ming looked at the stacks of books. As she walked up and down each aisle, she quickly became confused. The dark wood shelves seemed to grow taller with each step. The books all looked the same. Each row led to another row, which led to more stacks that contained even more brightly colored books. "What have I gotten myself into?" she thought to herself. Time ticked by, and, just when it seemed as though Ming would never find another human being in the maze of books, she stumbled upon a sales clerk.

2   The clerk's bright yellow T-shirt read, "Let Me Help You." Ming couldn't have been more pleased. "Just in time," she thought to herself. "I was about to give up on this place." Mother's Day was just around the corner, and Ming was on the hunt for the perfect gift. There was just one problem: Ming had no idea what type of book she wanted to buy.

3   Ming and the clerk chatted for a moment or two. Then, the lady in the yellow shirt had an idea. "When you were a little girl, did your mom like to read you stories?" Ming nodded. "You should pick out your favorite storybook. It will remind the two of you of your special memories. I'll help you write a special thank-you note on the inside cover. Your mom will love it!" The clerk spoke so quickly that Ming didn't have time to object.

4   The clerk was very enthusiastic as she marched Ming toward the children's book corner. Ming wasn't too sure about the idea, but her time at the bookstore had been unproductive so far. At least she was closer to finding something. After trotting through a few more rows of the dark stacks, Ming was happy to reach the children's area. The white stacks were the perfect height. Ming could even reach the top rows. The book titles were familiar, and the carpet beneath her feet featured white clouds in a blue sky.

5   The clerk sat patiently in a rocking chair, and Ming looked over the shelves. Some of the books she had seen before; others seemed brand new. Ming carefully studied the titles, but it wasn't until she reached the very bottom row that she found a copy of *The Magic of Myra Brown*. "This is it," she thought. The cover featured a freckle-faced redhead who wore a crooked witch's hat. A small black cat peered around Myra's leg, and the title stood out in bold red letters. "I'll take this one," she said to the clerk.

6   Ming pulled a wad of crumpled money from her jacket pocket. The clerk rang up the book, then found a special pen for Ming's inscription. Ming thought for a moment before writing, "Mom: Thank you for always making me feel as magical as Myra. Love, Ming."

7   "Perfect," said the clerk.

8   "Thank you so much," Ming replied. She held the book tightly as she made her way out the door. Ming was proud of the special gift. She couldn't wait for Mother's Day to arrive.

Emaline's Father's Day Search

9   Hi everyone. My name is Emaline, but you can call me Emma. Today, I am going to tell the story of the hardest thing I've had to do this year. It wasn't a test or a school project; the hardest thing I've done this year is search for a Father's Day present. I learned a lot from my search, and I want to pass along some advice to keep you from making the same mistake I made.

10   I guess maybe I shouldn't have waited until the last minute to start shopping, but I was really busy. So, on the day before Father's Day, I started my search. Of course, when I started, I didn't realize it was going to be a search. I thought the perfect gift would simply jump out at me, and I would be on my way home.

11   When I got to the mall, it was already filled with shoppers. I couldn't believe how many people were there! I took a deep breath and started to move with the crowd. I had a list of stores in my mind, and I was sure the perfect gift would be waiting at one of them. However, at each of the stores, I was greeted with the same situation: the special "Father's Day" section that had been set up was nearly empty. All that was left anywhere were silly little joke gifts, and none of these even came close to being the perfect gift I was hoping to find.

12   After hours of searching, I started my walk home empty-handed. I had failed in my search to find the perfect gift. Instead, my dad was going to be getting yet another card made from construction paper for Father's Day. I knew he wouldn't mind, but I sure did. I shouldn't have waited until the last minute to start shopping. I should have had an idea in mind when I set out. These two things, I've decided, are the most important things to remember when you are buying a gift, so I want to pass them along as tips for gift-buying success.

13   So to all the kids out there, this message is for you! Don't put things off the way I did. If you're looking for the perfect gift, you have to do some planning first. Plan ahead and get started early, and hopefully your search will have a happier ending than mine did.

19 For her best friend's birthday, Ming would probably –

⬭ **A** forget to buy a gift

⬭ **B** spend time searching for the perfect gift

⬭ **C** buy a gift her friend wouldn't like

⬭ **D** make someone else choose the gift

20 Based on Emma's actions in the passage, which of the following would be the most likely to happen?

⬭ **A** Emma does all her chores before she is asked.

⬭ **B** Emma turns in homework assignments before they are due.

⬭ **C** Emma is always the first person to finish school projects.

⬭ **D** Emma waits until the last minute to start school projects.

GO ON ▶

21 The author of "The Gift" most likely wrote this passage to –

    A inform the reader about types of Mother's Day gifts

    B persuade the reader to shop at bookstores for Mother's Day gifts

    C entertain the reader with a story about a girl buying a Mother's Day gift

    D express the author's thoughts about Mother's Day gifts

22 The author of "Emaline's Father's Day Search" is writing to –

    A explain to other kids where they should buy gifts

    B entertain readers with a funny story about buying a gift

    C inform readers about the history of Father's Day gifts

    D persuade other kids to start shopping before the last minute

23 What is similar about these two passages?

    A Both are about someone who is having trouble finding the perfect gift.

    B Both are about someone who is shopping in a bookstore.

    C Both are about someone who is looking for a Father's Day gift at the mall.

    D Both are about someone who waits too long to start shopping.

24 What is different about the two girls at the end of each passage?

⬭ A Ming is unhappy with her find; Emma is proud of the result of her search.

⬭ B Ming is proud of her find; Emma is unhappy with the result of her search.

⬭ C Ming doesn't think she has found the perfect gift; Emma thinks the gift she has found is perfect.

⬭ D Ming finds her perfect gift at the bookstore; Emma finds her perfect gift at the mall.

25 The author of "Emaline's Father's Day Search" is talking to –

⬭ A owners of stores at the mall

⬭ B fathers whose kids are buying gifts

⬭ C people who do all their shopping ahead of time

⬭ D people about her age who are shopping for gifts

26 If Emma had found the perfect gift on her search, how would her attitude most likely be different?

⬭ A She wouldn't think shopping at the mall was a good idea.

⬭ B She wouldn't think so many shoppers should be at the mall.

⬭ C She wouldn't think waiting until the last minute was such a bad idea.

⬭ D She wouldn't think anyone should try to find the perfect gift.

KIDS! Don't Miss This!

1   Diego nearly broke into a run to get to science class on the last Friday before spring vacation. Science was his least favorite subject, but it was also the last class of the day. After that, not only would he be free for over a week, but he would also be leaving the next day for a trip with his best friend, Agustin. Along with Agustin's family, the two friends were going to spend three days at their favorite amusement park. Diego couldn't wait for the day to be over.

2   As he walked toward his desk, Diego saw a paper lying face down on top. His stomach jumped. The test! He had hated taking last week's science test so much that he had put it out of his mind. This was the test that was going to determine his science grade; he couldn't get anything lower than a C if he wanted to pass. With a shaking hand, Diego turned the paper over. A bright red letter D stared at him from the top right corner.

3   At that moment, Mrs. Miller, his science teacher, entered the room. Diego hurried up to his teacher's desk. The only thing that could save his grade was extra credit. He gave this request to Mrs. Miller in a few rushed sentences. She thought for a few seconds, then picked up a paper from the stack on her desk and handed it to Diego.

4   "Normally," she told him, "I don't like to give extra credit, so your assignment isn't going to be easy. I want you to go to this exhibit and spend at least a few hours there. Pick two of the types of homes and write a paper comparing them. You will have to spend some time studying the exhibits, and you will have to do research at the library as well." Diego thanked his teacher and returned to his desk to read the paper.

KIDS! Don't Miss This!

5   Human beings aren't the only ones who build homes. All kinds of animals and insects create their own special dwellings. Whether you realize it or not, our world is covered with many different types of homes in many different places. The variety is fascinating! That's why you don't want to miss the "Homebodies" exhibit.

6   Sponsored by the Science Club, this event will be held Saturday and Sunday, from 1:00 p.m. until 5:00 p.m. each day. You will find all the wonderful exhibits in the Beechman Elementary School gym.

7   The Science Club has worked long and hard, and we know you're going to be impressed. This event is going to be fun, fun, fun!

8   You will learn how to make your very own:
- Spider webs
- Bird nests
- Beehives
- Ant farms
- Teepees
- Igloos
- Sod houses
- Log cabins
- Tents

9   You will see pictures from inside:
- Bear caves
- Lion dens
- Bat caves
- English castles
- Tree houses

10   And much, much more!

11   This is a great family event, and you won't want to miss a minute of it! Admission is free, so bring your parents, sisters, brothers, neighbors, and friends. Learn all about these exciting and different homes! Everyone will be there!

12   See you this weekend!

13   After he finished reading, Diego's gaze returned to the second paragraph. He couldn't believe his luck. He was going to have to choose between three fun-filled days with Agustin and passing science class. He could picture Agustin and his entire family speeding down the hill of a favorite roller coaster. With a sinking heart, he realized he did not see himself in that picture.

GO ON ▶

27 Which of the following would be the most likely conclusion to this story?

   ⬭ **A** Diego will skip the exhibit to go on the trip with Agustin and his family.

   ⬭ **B** Agustin will skip the trip and go to the exhibit with Diego.

   ⬭ **C** Agustin and his family will go on the trip, but Diego will stay home and go to the exhibit.

   ⬭ **D** Mrs. Miller will give Diego a different extra-credit assignment so he can go on the trip.

28 Mrs. Miller probably gave Diego a hard assignment because –

   ⬭ **A** she wants to make sure he spends some time learning about science

   ⬭ **B** she is a mean teacher who wants him to fail the class

   ⬭ **C** she doesn't want him to go on the trip with Agustin

   ⬭ **D** she is mad at Diego for not liking science

29 Which of the following statements from the passage is an opinion?

   ⬭ **A** *Our world is covered with many different types of homes in many different places.*

   ⬭ **B** *This event will be held Saturday and Sunday, from 1:00 p.m. until 5:00 p.m. each day.*

   ⬭ **C** *Admission is free.*

   ⬭ **D** *We know you're going to be impressed.*

30 Read the following sentence from the paper Mrs. Miller gave Diego.

   Learn all about these exciting and different homes!

Which word could be removed from this sentence to make it a fact?

   ⬭ **A** *learn*

   ⬭ **B** *exciting*

   ⬭ **C** *homes*

   ⬭ **D** *different*

GO ON ➡

Funds for Food

1   Jeanette reached into the dog cage and pulled out the newspaper. It was dirty and wet, and she made a face as the smell hit her nose. She loved working with the animals at the shelter, but, sometimes, the odors were a little overwhelming.

2   "Hey! Do you know where the rest of the cat food is?" asked Jessica, her twin sister, as she walked into the room. "I can only find one bag." The sisters were the best of friends and often did things together. Their favorite thing to do was to volunteer at the shelter with their mother. They went off in search of more pet food, but, instead of finding it, they found Mrs. Kline, the lady in charge of the shelter. She looked very unhappy.

3   "If you're looking for more food, there isn't any," she said. "We just don't have the money for it. Winter is just around the corner, and we've had so many new animals coming in; it's hard to keep up! I'm just not sure what we're going to do," she sighed.

4   Jeanette and Jessica found their mother in the laundry room, washing the animals' towels and blankets. Like her daughters, Mrs. Snowden was always hard at work when she was at the shelter. The twins told their mother the sad news.

5   "Do you think that there is something we could do to help, Mom?" asked Jeanette "Could we raise some money?" Mrs. Snowden smiled; she knew that when her girls got an idea to do something, they usually did it!

6   "Let's go talk with Mrs. Kline."

7   For the next two hours, the volunteers sat at the snack table and threw out all kinds of ideas for what could be done to help the shelter. Everything was discussed, and, in the end, they made plans for several fundraisers, including a bake sale, a car wash, and a yard sale. Mrs. Snowden took charge of the planning, working hard to make sure all the plans came together. Mrs. Kline made a few phone calls and arranged for the local radio and television stations to run some ads for the fundraisers.

8   The rest of the day was spent creating jars with pictures of the different pets glued onto them. Mrs. Snowden took the jars to area stores and asked the store owners to place the jars near the checkout counter. She hoped people would donate their extra change to the shelter. Another volunteer made posters. He hung them at local pet stores. The posters asked for donations of old blankets, towels, and play toys. This would help the shelter cut costs.

9   Jessica and Jeanette made their own plans. For the next month, they raised money every way they could. They had a yard sale and sold toys they no longer played with. They raked the autumn leaves for their neighbors and helped their grandma clean her house and make jam. They walked Mrs. Cotton's dogs each day, and they helped with the car wash. The girls kept their earnings in a jar labeled "Funds for Food."

10   At the end of the month, Mrs. Snowden took the girls and the funds to the grocery store. They loaded up the car with bags of pet food. Everyone had big smiles on their faces as they walked into the shelter. Mrs. Kline was pleased to hear about all the hard work the girls had done, and she had good news for them, too.

11   "I talked to members of the City Council. They were so impressed at how hard we were working to help the shelter, they agreed to give us a grant—a gift of money we can use to keep the shelter open and running. Isn't that wonderful?"

12   Everyone cheered, and the twins were given the best reward of all. They fed all the new puppies—and got licked as a "thank you."

31   Which of the following sentences tells you the twins are determined?

⬭ **A** *Mrs. Snowden smiled; she knew that when her girls got an idea to do something, they usually did it!*

⬭ **B** *The sisters were the best of friends and often did things together.*

⬭ **C** *The girls kept their earnings in a jar labeled "Funds for Food."*

⬭ **D** *Everyone cheered, and the twins were given the best reward of all.*

32   Which of the following was not a result of working to raise funds?

⬭ **A** The shelter received several boxes of used blankets.

⬭ **B** The City Council gave the shelter a grant.

⬭ **C** The Snowden family purchased food for the shelter.

⬭ **D** The volunteers were able to keep the shelter open.

GO ON ▶

33 How does Mrs. Kline's attitude at the beginning of the passage differ from the twins' attitude?

⬭ **A** Mrs. Kline wants to raise money for more food, but the twins don't think it will be possible.

⬭ **B** Mrs. Kline is unsure of what to do about the lack of food, but the twins think she should hire more volunteers.

⬭ **C** Mrs. Kline thinks she should close the shelter, but the twins think she should keep it open.

⬭ **D** Mrs. Kline is unsure of what to do about the lack of food, but the twins have an idea right away.

34 How do Mrs. Snowden's actions when working at the shelter compare to her actions during fundraising?

⬭ **A** She does laundry at the shelter, and she does laundry to raise money.

⬭ **B** She doesn't do any work at the shelter, and she doesn't help with the fundraising.

⬭ **C** She works hard at the shelter, and she does a lot of work to plan the fundraising.

⬭ **D** She makes signs for the shelter, and she makes signs to help with the fundraising.

School Uniforms

by Amber Gianetti
Lakewood Elementary School

1   Last year, the school board decided Lakewood Elementary students should wear uniforms. Many parents think this is best for kids. We have to wear uniforms to school every day because somebody's mom thinks it's better for us. But, in reality, school uniforms are really bad for our mental health. No one wants to wear the same thing every day, especially when it makes them look just like everyone else.

2   Our uniforms are boring. We wear polo shirts or button-down shirts, and they have to be light blue or white. The boys wear khaki pants and brown shoes. The girls wear brown shoes and a khaki skirt. Every day, we get up and put on the same old boring clothes.

3   I've talked with many of my friends. They all said putting on the same outfit every day is really depressing. We don't want to go to school depressed. It's hard to get our work done. All our creativity is drained.

4   Our hallways are filled with students who all look the same. According to my teacher, the uniforms remind us we are all equal. While I don't disagree that we are all equal, I think people send this message, not clothes. The uniforms cover up each student's uniqueness. Even though we are all equal, we are all distinct. There are differences in our school, and I think we should be allowed to wear clothes we have picked out in order to express our unique qualities. Haven't we always been told that it doesn't matter what's on the outside; it's what's inside that counts?

5   If teachers think uniforms are such a great idea, why don't they wear them? Lakewood teachers wear whatever they want. They are allowed to express themselves with an individual sense of style. If the teachers had to wear the same outfit each day, I know they would feel differently about the uniform rule.

6   Uniforms are bad for our mental health. The uniforms tell us we have to look the same to be equal and we shouldn't express who we are. Kids shouldn't have to wear uniforms to school. We should be allowed to make our own decisions about what to wear every day.

35   How does the author of "School Uniforms" organize paragraphs 2-5?

    ⬭ **A**   Each paragraph presents a cause and an effect of wearing uniforms.

    ⬭ **B**   Each paragraph gives a description of one part of the uniform.

    ⬭ **C**   Each paragraph compares and contrasts the uniforms with regular clothes.

    ⬭ **D**   Each paragraph tells a different problem the author has with the uniforms.

36   All of the author's problems with the uniforms are connected by the idea that –

    ⬭ **A**   students have to wear uniforms, but teachers don't

    ⬭ **B**   students have to wear the same clothes every day, and all students look the same

    ⬭ **C**   the colors in the uniforms are boring, and they make students depressed

    ⬭ **D**   the boys are allowed to wear polo shirts, but the girls are not

Directions for Assessment 2

Assessment 2 includes multiple-choice questions. For a multiple-choice question, fill in one answer bubble to mark the correct answer.

Read each selection and each question carefully. If you do not know an answer, you may skip the question and come back to it later.

When you finish, check your answers.

New Kid in Town

1   Tony felt like the shortest boy in class, and, to make matters worse, he was the new kid on the block! Making friends wasn't the easiest thing to do in a new school. His mother told him he would fit right in with the other children, but, for some reason, he just wasn't sure.

2   During homeroom, a brown-haired boy wearing a gray T-shirt said "Hi" to Tony, but none of the other kids seemed to notice him. When the teacher called out his last name, she <u>mispronounced</u> it, and everyone laughed. Tony lowered his head and stared at the top of his desk. He didn't want to see the kids laughing at him; the sound of their laughter was bad enough. The teacher began her morning lesson. Tony couldn't focus. "This couldn't move any slower," he thought to himself. Time slowly crept by. Every so often, Tony would peek up at the clock. He was careful not to let his eyes move off the desk for very long.

3   Tony wasn't sure of the new school's schedule, so the ringing lunch bell surprised him. The new student walked down the hall to his locker and put his books away. In the cafeteria, he went through the line and got his tray. He found a table near the window and sat alone. The air around him felt cold, unlike his old school, which always felt warm and inviting. "If only I could go back to my old school," he wished to himself as he ate another bite of pizza. "I'd have all of my old friends, and everything would be back to normal," he thought.

4   Changing schools had been hard for Tony. His father had taken a new job halfway through the school year. Tony had to say goodbye to his friends, to his teachers, and to the only home he had ever known. Tony didn't want to finish his lunch. He knew as soon as he did, he would have to make his way to the playground. He would watch all the other kids have fun as he stood off to the side. "I wonder if I can sit here until it's time to go back to class," he thought.

5   Tony took a look out the window. A group of boys from homeroom was playing kickball on the playground. The lunch monitor strolled past Tony and gave him a look that suggested he had better move along soon. He finished his milk and got up to put away his trash. Tony put on his coat, shoved his hands deep into his pockets, and headed out to watch the crowd. He sought out a place by the fence and slumped down to sit on the ground. He kept his head buried.

6   "Hey! Hey you!" At first Tony didn't realize the voice was calling out for him. "You're the new kid, aren't you?" the boy in the gray T-shirt shouted.

7   "Yeah, I'm Tony." He lifted his eyes and squinted as the sunlight hit his face. He was afraid the boy would make fun of him by mispronouncing his last name the way his teacher had.

8   The boy ran to where Tony was sitting. "I'm Solomon, but everyone just calls me Solo. I'm going to play kickball with the other guys. We need another player to make the teams even. Do you know how to play kickball?"

9   "Yeah, sure," he replied.

10   "Great!" Solo said. Solo reached out his hand and pulled Tony to his feet. Tony realized he wasn't the shortest kid in class. He and Solo stood eye to eye. The boys ran toward the makeshift field. "Tony's gonna play," Solo yelled. Tony was worried someone would object, but the only words anyone uttered were, "Next up!"

11   Tony took his seat with his team. The boys started quizzing him on his old school and where he used to live. Everyone was interested in what he had to say, and he appreciated the attention. The kickball game ended with a winning run scored by Tony's team. As the boys celebrated, Tony realized being a new kid in town wasn't so bad after all.

1   Which of the following is the best summary of the passage?

    A A boy named Tony is nervous about starting a new school in the middle of the year. At first, he misses his old school and doesn't think he fits in. Later, a group of boys invites him to play kickball, and he begins to feel welcome.

    B A boy named Tony is the shortest kid at his new school. The teacher and the other students make fun of him and mispronounce his name. When he is eating lunch, he decides his new school is colder than his old school.

    C Tony, a new student at school, spends most of his first day staring at his desk. Sometimes, he looks at the clock, which is moving very slowly. Later, at recess, Tony sits by the fence and watches other boys play kickball.

    D Tony, a new student at school, makes friends with a boy named Solomon. Solomon wears a gray T-shirt and stands eye to eye with Tony. Tony is happy because he scores the winning run in the kickball game.

2   Who helps solve Tony's problem?

    A his mother

    B his homeroom teacher

    C Solomon

    D his father

3   Which of the following would Tony be most likely to do if another new kid came to the class?

    A Tony would invite the new kid to play kickball on the playground.

    B Tony would laugh at the new kid in the cafeteria.

    C Tony would mispronounce the new kid's name to make fun of him.

    D Tony would tell the new kid not to make friends with Solomon.

4   Read this sentence from paragraph 2.

When the teacher called out his last name, she <u>mispronounced</u> it, and everyone laughed.

What does <u>mispronounced</u> mean?

⬭ **A** spelled the wrong way

⬭ **B** said the wrong way

⬭ **C** said the correct way

⬭ **D** spelled the correct way

5   How would this story most likely be different if it took place at the beginning of the school year?

⬭ **A** The teacher would not mispronounce Tony's name.

⬭ **B** None of the students would play kickball.

⬭ **C** Tony's father would not have to get a new job.

⬭ **D** There might be other new students in Tony's class.

6   According to the passage, Tony –

⬭ **A** is the shortest kid in school

⬭ **B** is happy to be at the new school

⬭ **C** is the same height as Solomon

⬭ **D** wears a gray T-shirt

7   Read this sentence from paragraph 2.

Tony lowered his head and stared at the top of his desk.

Why does Tony stare at his desk?

⬭ **A** He can't read the board.

⬭ **B** He doesn't want to look at the kids who are laughing at him.

⬭ **C** He doesn't want to look out the window and see kids playing kickball.

⬭ **D** He wants to read a book instead of listening to the teacher's lesson.

GO ON ▶

84

On the Hunt for a Fossil

1   Have you ever wanted to be a fossilist? Human beings have been searching for fossils for centuries. Fossilists are people who search for fossils. Fossils are the remains of centuries-old plants and animals that have been preserved. Fossils are oftentimes found in sedimentary rock. Sedimentary rock is formed when layers of dirt are compacted together. Examples of sedimentary rock include limestone, sandstone, and shale. Fossils have also been discovered in amber (a yellowish-brown, see-through substance made of hardened sap), ice, and asphalt (a black, tar-like substance used for paving roads). Some of the oldest fossils can be as old as 3.5 billion years. Newer fossils are about 10,000 years old.

2   Paleontologists and fossilists are people who seek out and study fossils and other organic remains. They have gone all over the world looking for these rare <u>relics</u>. Fossils can be found around the globe, from Greenland to Antarctica and everywhere in between. Modern-day paleontologists carry special tools with them, including chipping hammers, chisels, collecting bags, gloves, eye protection, soft brushes, special maps  and computers, and small shovels called trowels. They also bring along magnifying glasses so they can see tiny things more clearly. Most also carry notebooks for recording information.

3   Fossilists haven't always had the benefit of maps and special tools, however. Long ago, fossil hunters had to rely on their senses as well as on keen observation. One person known for her early fossil-hunting skills was Mary Anning. She was born in 1799, and her family was very poor, especially after the death of her father in 1810. As a teenager, Mary would often walk the <u>unstable</u> cliffs near her home of Lyme Regis, England, in search of fossils. She collected fossils and sold them to scientists, to collectors, and to museums in order to make money. As her knowledge of fossils and their origins grew, she demonstrated her talents as a well-skilled fossil hunter.

4   Some scientists credit Mary with early discoveries of ichthyosaur and plesiosaurus fossils. Both finds were considered extremely important to the scientific community. Despite her refined talent, Mary had to sell her findings in order to survive. It wasn't until much later in her life that Anning received the recognition she deserved. In 1838, she received wages from the British Association for the Advancement of Science. At around this time, she also received money from the Geological Society of London so she could pay her living expenses. Until her death in 1847, Mary, or "Fossil Woman," as she became known, searched for fossils. During her lifetime, she made important discoveries, including the skeletons of sea serpents and flying dinosaurs.

5   Today, both professionals and beginners enjoy fossil hunting. Although it isn't easy, the search is thrilling. Next time you're out in the backyard, you should take an extra close look at any rocks you find. Maybe you will be the next Mary Anning!

A Modern-Day Fossilist's Checklist

6

7

A Modern-Day Fossilist's Checklist

So you want to be a fossilist! Here are a few things every fossilist needs. Having the right tools and the right information is important, especially if you want to bring home more than a few broken stones. Remember to talk with your parents before you decide to do any work as a fossilist. There are many tools you will need their permission to use. After discussing this exciting hobby, maybe you'll get your mom and dad excited about fossils, too.

☐ Geologist's Rock Pick: the square end will break up rock, while the pick end will help you dig

☐ Chipping Hammer: this hammer has a flat blade that is useful for splitting or trimming rock

☐ Chisel: smaller than a chipping hammer, this tool comes in a variety of sizes; it is also good for splitting and trimming smaller rocks

☐ Safety Goggles & Gloves: important forms of protection when cutting rock

☐ Tweezers: very useful when removing very small pieces

☐ Trowel: helpful for digging soft earth

☐ Soft Brush: the brush will dust off your search site

☐ Compass: will help you find your way

☐ Maps: used to identify where you've been and where you're going

☐ Measurement Device: you many want to measure the size of your find

☐ Magnifying Glass: useful for looking at the smallest details

☐ Camera: you may want to take pictures of your find

☐ Notebook & Pencil: for taking notes

☐ Collecting Bags: plastic bags work just fine; use these to store your fossils

☐ Books & Other Resources: field guides will help you identify areas with many fossils; they may also help you identify what you have found; do some research on fossil hunting before you begin–they will discuss techniques for digging, searching, and collecting

8   The author of "A Modern-Day Fossilist's Checklist" most likely –

⬯ **A**   has no interest in fossils

⬯ **B**   thinks collecting fossils is a fun hobby

⬯ **C**   dislikes collecting fossils

⬯ **D**   is famous for collecting fossils

9   Read the following sentence from paragraph 6 of "A Modern-Day Fossilist's Checklist."

After discussing this exciting hobby, maybe you'll get your mom and dad excited about fossils, too.

Which word from this sentence makes it an opinion?

⬭ **A** *fossils*

⬭ **B** *discussing*

⬭ **C** *exciting*

⬭ **D** *hobby*

10   What is the main idea of paragraph 2?

⬭ **A** Using special tools, fossilists look for fossils all over the world.

⬭ **B** Modern-day paleontologists use magnifying glasses to see things more clearly.

⬭ **C** Using special tools, fossilists look for fossils in Greenland and Antarctica.

⬭ **D** Modern-day paleontologists carry notebooks all over the world while looking for fossils.

11   Read the following sentence from paragraph 3.

As a teenager, Mary would often walk the <u>unstable</u> cliffs near her home of Lyme Regis, England, in search of fossils.

What does <u>unstable</u> mean?

⬭ **A** very steady

⬭ **B** not steady

⬭ **C** not easily moved

⬭ **D** not changed

12 In paragraph 2, <u>relics</u> are –

⬭ **A** tools used by fossilists

⬭ **B** new objects

⬭ **C** places on the globe

⬭ **D** objects from the past

13 Which of the following sentences from "On the Hunt for a Fossil" is not an opinion?

⬭ **A** *Some scientists credit Mary with early discoveries of ichthyosaur and plesiosaurus fossils.*

⬭ **B** *Next time you're out in the backyard, you should take an extra close look at any rocks you find.*

⬭ **C** *It wasn't until much later in her life that Anning received the recognition she deserved.*

⬭ **D** *Although it isn't easy, the search is thrilling.*

14 Why did Mary Anning first hunt for fossils?

⬭ **A** The Geological Society of London paid her to look for fossils.

⬭ **B** The British Association for the Advancement of Science wanted her to find fossils.

⬭ **C** She sold the fossils she found in order to support her family.

⬭ **D** She enjoyed discovering the fossils for her private collection.

Go West, I Say, Go West!

1   Slowly, the man walked down the dirt street, right through the middle of town. He knew everyone's eyes were on him as he strolled proudly toward the general store. Eyes peeked at him from second-story windows. There were multiple faces visible through every open doorway, and no one on the wooden sidewalks had moved a step since the man had appeared. His clothes and his walk told everyone he was a rich man—a rich man with something to say.

2   It seemed as though the entire town was holding its breath as he climbed up on the back of a wagon and called for everyone's attention. The words "General Store" loomed over his raised arms. Even the horses seemed to turn their heads to the side so they could listen.

3   "Ladies and gentlemen!" he cried out. "I am here today to ask you an important question. It's a simple question—one you have probably already asked yourselves."

4   In the small Eastern town, the only sounds heard were those of women's skirts rustling and of men's boots scraping as people crowded closer to hear what the rich man was going to say next.

5   "The question is . . ." he paused, making sure that all eyes were looking at him and only him.

6   "Are you happy? That's it. Are you happy?" He lowered his arms to his knees, bending them slightly. He looked at the eyes of the crowd, panning his gaze back and forth.

7   The crowd began to mumble softly; women whispered, men chuckled.

8   "Are you?" he asked again, raising his arms a second time and shouting more loudly than the first time. "Maybe you're just waiting and hoping for happiness? For a new start? For a new beginning? If you're tired of waiting and hoping, I have the answer for you! Get away from this dry place. Leave these harsh winters behind. Forget your barren fields and your tired forests."

9   The crowd's mumbling grew louder, and people began to move around, shifting from foot to foot. They were curious, anxious, and unsure—all rolled into one.

10   "It's time for you to go west!" shouted the man. "Go west where you can have land to call your own. Soon, we will be halfway through the 19th century, and the place to be is in California! Imagine a place where the land is so rich, you can grow anything. There are forests full of trees, and the hunting is plentiful! The weather is pleasant, and water is always close by. What are you waiting for?"

GO ON ▶

11   Voices could be heard now as people talked to each other and leaned to whisper in each other's ears. Was this the truth? Could the man be lying? But he was dressed so nicely. Why hadn't they heard about the wonders of this new place until now? California was a site for gold rushers, but many of the townspeople had never heard of all the other pleasantries mentioned by the man.

12   "Almost a thousand people have already made the trip!" continued the man. "I'm here to make sure you STOP talking about it and START doing it. Saddle up your horses! Load up your wagons! Head out today on the California Trail! The first wagon train leaves tomorrow!"

13   "Wait a minute!" shouted a man from the front of the crowd. "Is California a state yet?"

14   "Just about!" replied the mysterious man. "It will happen before the year is out."

15   "Isn't California was just for gold rushers?" asked a young man. Heads began to nod and murmurs of agreement were heard.

16   "Gold? Yes, of course there's gold!" he replied. "Rivers full of it, just waiting for you to find it and make your fortune."

17   "Is there enough good land for everyone?" asked a woman with a child on her hip.

18   "Ma'am, there's more land than they know what to do with. It's cheap land. Some of it is even free!" Excitement ran through the crowd now. The word "free" echoed among the whispers.

19   "Enough!" shouted the man and silence returned. "The first wagon train leaves tomorrow at noon. If you want to go, be here an hour earlier with your family and your belongings. Your future is waiting to begin!"

20   With that, the man jumped down from the wagon. Members of the crowd called out to him, but he let their questions sting his back as he walked away. By morning, more than half the townspeople, with dreams of all-new beginnings on their minds, were lined up behind the rich man's wagon. With a crack of his reins, the wagon train began to move.

---

15 Why do so many townspeople decide to follow the rich man?

⬭ **A** They want to work for the rich man.

⬭ **B** The rich man has promised a better life in the South.

⬭ **C** They can't find work in the Eastern town.

⬭ **D** The rich man has promised a better life in the West.

16 When does this story take place?

⬭ **A** about 150 years in the future

⬭ **B** in the present

⬭ **C** about 1,500 years ago

⬭ **D** about 150 years ago

17 According to the rich man, how is life in the West different than life in the Eastern town?

⬭ **A** Land in the West is expensive because it is good for farming, but land in the East is cheap.

⬭ **B** People are happier in the East than they are in the West.

⬭ **C** The weather in the West is pleasant, while there are harsh winters in the East.

⬭ **D** There are forests full of trees in the East, but, in the West, there is rich farmland.

18 Which sentence from the passage gives one reason why the townspeople doubted the rich man at first?

⬭ **A** *Voices could be heard now as people talked to each other and leaned to whisper in each other's ears.*

⬭ **B** *California was a site for gold rushers, but many of the townspeople had never heard of all the other pleasantries mentioned by the man.*

⬭ **C** *They were curious, anxious, and unsure—all rolled into one.*

⬭ **D** *But he was dressed so nicely.*

19 In general, does the rich man get his point across to the townspeople?

⬭ **A** Yes; more than half of them decide to go West.

⬭ **B** No; more than half of them decide not to go West.

⬭ **C** No; some of them don't believe there is gold in California.

⬭ **D** Yes; they all decide they want cheap land in California.

20 Why is the man dressed in fancy clothes?

⬭ **A** People are more likely to believe him if he is dressed nicely.

⬭ **B** He likes to dress in fancy clothes.

⬭ **C** He lost his work clothes and has to wear nice clothes.

⬭ **D** It is cold outside, and his nice clothes are warm.

21 Read the following sentence from paragraph 2.

It seemed as though the entire town was holding its breath as he climbed up on the back of a wagon and called for everyone's attention.

The best word to describe the townspeople at this point is –

⬭ **A** angry

⬭ **B** afraid

⬭ **C** curious

⬭ **D** uninterested

GO ON ➤

Soccer

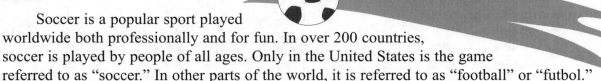

1   Soccer is a popular sport played worldwide both professionally and for fun. In over 200 countries, soccer is played by people of all ages. Only in the United States is the game referred to as "soccer." In other parts of the world, it is referred to as "football" or "futbol."

2   Historians have found evidence that suggests ancient people made up and participated in different kicking games similar to soccer. The game of soccer as we know it today began in England around the 19th century. Official rules were written for games involving ball handling in the late 1800s, and, at that time, the game allowed for greater use of the hands than is permitted with modern soccer. A meeting of the London Football Associate in 1863, however, split football into two sports. The first was rugby football, which is the parent sport of American football. This game allowed for touching and carrying the ball. The second sport was association football, or soccer, which did not allow the use of the hands.

3   Throughout the rest of the 1800s, soccer's popularity was widespread in England and Scotland. British traders, sailors, and soldiers carried the sport to Germany, Italy, Austria, and South America. In 1904, the Federation Internationale de Football Association (FIFA) was formed. FIFA is still the worldwide governing body of soccer. In 1930, FIFA organized the first World Cup, soccer's premier tournament that is held every four years.

4   Soccer was not always such a popular sport in America. While many other countries throughout Europe and South America embraced the game of soccer, people in the United States were slow to <u>accept</u> the sport. It wasn't until the 1970s that the North American Soccer League gained the interest of fans in the U.S. Although the league eventually went out of business because of financial problems, it left a lasting impression on Americans, particularly among young people. Today, soccer is the fastest-growing high school and college sport in the United States.

22   Which of the following happened before football was split into two sports in 1863?

⬭ **A** People played kicking games similar to soccer.

⬭ **B** People in the United States became more interested in soccer.

⬭ **C** The game of rugby football was created.

⬭ **D** The first World Cup was organized by FIFA.

23 Look at this web about soccer.

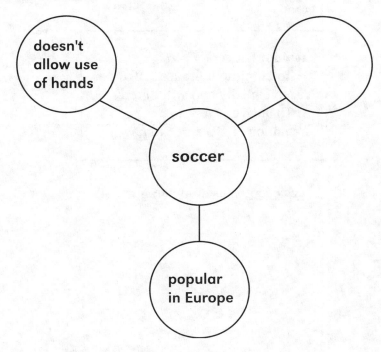

Which of the following belongs in the empty circle?

⬭ **A** allows for young players only

⬭ **B** allows for carrying the ball

⬭ **C** also called rugby football

⬭ **D** also called association football

24 How does the author of "Soccer" organize paragraphs 2-4?

⬭ **A** by giving the history of soccer in time order

⬭ **B** by comparing and contrasting two types of soccer

⬭ **C** by describing the game of soccer

⬭ **D** by listing the problems of the North American Soccer League, then giving solutions

GO ON ➤

25 Read the meanings below for the word <u>accept</u>.

> **ac•cept** (ak sept´) *verb*
> **1.** To admit to a group **2.** To receive gladly and with interest **3.** To answer "yes" to an invitation **4.** To agree to pay

Which meaning best fits the way <u>accept</u> is used in paragraph 4?

⬭ **A** Meaning 1

⬭ **B** Meaning 2

⬭ **C** Meaning 3

⬭ **D** Meaning 4

26 The author of this passage most likely wrote it to –

⬭ **A** explain the rules of soccer

⬭ **B** entertain readers with funny stories about soccer

⬭ **C** inform readers about the history of soccer

⬭ **D** persuade readers to join a soccer team

27 Read the first sentence of the summary below.

> Soccer is a sport played in many parts of the world.

Which of the following best completes the summary?

- ⬭ **A** Many historians believe ancient people played games that were similar to the modern sport of soccer. Soccer did not have official rules until the 1800s, and the official rules allowed players to use their hands.

- ⬭ **B** The original sport of soccer was split into two sports by the London Football Associate, and one of these sports was called rugby football. FIFA, soccer's worldwide governing body, was formed in 1904. In 1930, FIFA held the first World Cup.

- ⬭ **C** British traders, sailors, and soldiers brought the sport to other countries and made it popular in many parts of the world. However, they did not bring it to the United States. Soccer did not become popular in the United States until the 1970s.

- ⬭ **D** Modern soccer began in England, where it was later split into two sports. After that, it gained popularity, and a worldwide governing body was formed. Recently, the sport has gained popularity in the United States.

28 Which of the following sentences from the passage tells you why soccer is such a fast-growing high school and college sport in the United States?

- ⬭ **A** *While many other countries throughout Europe and South America embraced the game of soccer, people in the United States were slow to accept the sport.*

- ⬭ **B** *Although the league eventually went out of business because of financial problems, it left a lasting impression on Americans, particularly among young people.*

- ⬭ **C** *Historians have found evidence that suggests ancient people made up and participated in different kicking games similar to soccer.*

- ⬭ **D** *In 1930, FIFA organized the first World Cup, soccer's premier tournament that is held every four years.*

GO ON

Samantha's Story

1   Every day, Samantha stared out the front window at 10:00 a.m. That's when the mailman slowly pulled his truck up to the mailbox and dropped off the Perkins' mail. As soon as the white square vehicle headed to the next house, Sam was out the door. She rushed down the brick sidewalk, swung open the white picket fence, and pulled down the mailbox door. She examined the contents as she made her way back to the house. Each day for the past five days, she had found nothing with her name on it. This day was different, however. The inside of the mailbox was crowded. A large, brown envelope took up most of the space inside the metal box. She tugged at the stack of mail, freeing the envelope, her envelope. The label on the front read: Samantha Perkins.

2   Finally, the information packet from the Hillsboro Summer Fun Camp had arrived. She had been expecting this bundle for a week. Sam couldn't wait to get inside. She wanted to tear into the brown paper right there in the front yard, but it was windy and she didn't want to lose any of the information.

3   She rushed to the house and made her way to the kitchen. She opened the envelope and carefully laid out its contents on the table. She found a welcome letter, a daily program, and a list of activities. Samantha was a little nervous about going to a place so far away, but, once she saw all the activities, she knew it would be fun. As she looked through each piece, she started to daydream about summer camp.

Toral's Story

4   The sight of the mail truck pulling up to her house every day filled Toral with fear. Each morning at 9:30 a.m., she would kneel next to the front window and wait for the mail to arrive. After the mail truck moved on down the street, Toral would rise slowly and begin the long walk to the mailbox. Even though the mailbox was only across the street, the journey seemed to take forever. Finally, she would reach the shiny black box and pull open the door. Each day for the past five days, the box had held only mail for Toral's parents: bills, catalogs, and junk mail. This day was different, however. There were no catalogs or white envelopes; there was only a single brown envelope that filled up most of the space inside the mailbox. Toral knew it was for her, but she didn't want to remove it. Finally, she reached in and pulled the envelope out far enough to read the label on the front: Toral Johnson.

5   With a sinking heart, Toral took her envelope and headed back to the house. The clouds in the sky were gray to match her mood, and a strong wind blew her hair in swirls around her face. She thought about opening the envelope right there. She could imagine its contents being carried away in the wind. In the end, though, she knew that even losing the information would not save her. Her parents would just get another copy.

6   Toral's pace slowed even more after she entered the house. She finally made her way to the kitchen table, where she peeled open the envelope's seal and dumped its contents on the table. A welcome letter, a daily program, and a list of activities stared up at her. All had the words Hillsboro Summer Fun Camp printed at the top. Toral sighed. There was no longer a way to pretend it might not happen. She was going to summer camp.

GO ON ▶

29   What is similar about these two passages?

⭕ **A** Both are about girls who enjoy waiting for the mail to arrive.

⭕ **B** Both are about girls who like to daydream.

⭕ **C** Both are about girls who are in a bad mood.

⭕ **D** Both are about girls who are waiting for an envelope.

30   How is the topic of summer camp presented in these two passages?

⭕ **A** Both passages talk about summer camp in a negative way.

⭕ **B** Both passages talk about summer camp in a positive way.

⭕ **C** Samantha's story talks about summer camp in a positive way; Toral's story talks about it in a negative way.

⭕ **D** Samantha's story talks about summer camp in a negative way; Toral's story talks about it in a positive way.

31   In paragraph 2 of "Samantha's Story," why is Samantha in a hurry to get inside?

⭕ **A** She wants to open the brown envelope.

⭕ **B** She doesn't like to be outside in the wind.

⭕ **C** She is nervous about going to camp.

⭕ **D** She wants to bring the rest of the mail to her parents.

32   How is the passage "Toral's Story" organized?

⭕ **A** It lists the causes of Toral going to summer camp, then the effects.

⭕ **B** It tells about Toral's problem of summer camp, then gives a solution.

⭕ **C** It describes a number of things about the summer camp Toral is going to.

⭕ **D** It tells the story, in time order, of Toral getting her summer camp information.

33   According to the passages, what is the connection between Samantha and Toral?

    ◯ **A** They have the same mailman.

    ◯ **B** They are going to the same summer camp.

    ◯ **C** They are friends from school.

    ◯ **D** They both have white picket fences.

34   How do Samantha and Toral act differently when they are getting the mail?

    ◯ **A** Samantha rushes to the mailbox, but Toral makes the walk slowly.

    ◯ **B** Samantha swings open the gate to her fence, but Toral opens her gate slowly.

    ◯ **C** Toral takes a long time to cross her street, but Samantha runs across quickly.

    ◯ **D** Toral rushes through the mail to look for her envelope, but Samantha looks at everything slowly.

35   Which of the following sentences lets you know Samantha is excited about summer camp?

    ◯ **A** *She opened the envelope and carefully laid out its contents on the table.*

    ◯ **B** *As she looked through each piece, she started to daydream about summer camp.*

    ◯ **C** *She found a welcome letter, a daily program, and a list of activities.*

    ◯ **D** *A large, brown envelope took up most of the space inside the metal box.*

Summer Fun

1   "Wake up!" Meredith shouted at her sleeping brother. "Today is the first day of summer vacation!" Meredith was anxious to start summer fun, but her brother had no interest in anything other than crawling under his soft sheets. Max mumbled something impossible to hear and rolled back over, pulling the comforter over his head.

2   "Mom says we can go to the wave pool if all our chores are done," Meredith said trying to persuade Max to get out of bed. "Mine are done, so get dressed and get moving. I want to get to the wave pool." She shut his bedroom door and skipped downstairs.

3   Meredith had been up since the crack of dawn. Summer held so many possibilities for fun; she couldn't wait to get started. Her bed was made; her floor was spotless. Her fifth-grade school books had been lined up neatly on the shelf. After finding a spot in her closet for her backpack, all Meredith could think about was summer fun. Her daydream was interrupted by a phone call. Meredith dashed into the kitchen to answer it: "Marshall residence."

4   "Hello. This is Amy. Is Meredith home?"

5   Meredith and Amy had been best friends since first grade and lived in the same neighborhood, just two blocks from each other.

6   "Hi, Amy! Can you believe it's really summer? What do you want to do today?" Meredith asked. "I was thinking about going to the wave pool. Do you want to go with us?" she asked.

7   "Cool. Let me check with my mom." Amy cupped her hand over the phone. "Mommm," she hollered. Even though the phone was covered, Meredith could still hear the voice. "Can I go to the wave pool with Meredith?"

GO ON

8   Amy knew what the response would be. Her room was a disaster area. Clothes had been thrown on the floor, her backpack and books were spread out on the desk, and CDs were scattered across the bed.

9   She came back to the phone with a response. "I can't go until my room is picked up," Amy said, "and it's a real mess!"

10   "How long do you think you'll be?" Meredith asked.

11   "Well, I think I can get it finished before you leave for the pool," Amy answered, mentally plotting where she could throw all her stuff–under the bed, in her closet, in her drawers, and other favorite hiding spots. "I can sort it all out later," she thought to herself.

12   Meredith knew better; she knew what Amy was planning. Amy was not tidy. She was the messiest person Meredith knew, and, if the girls wanted to get to the wave pool, Amy was going to need some help. "Amy, if you don't really clean your room today, you're going to have to face it another day. You'll probably spend most of the summer trying to get your room in order. I'll help you with your room today, and you can help me with some chores later this week. How's that sound?"

13   "Great!" Amy said excitedly. She knew Meredith was right, and she was <u>thankful</u> for some assistance. Amy was nothing like her neat and tidy best friend. In order to have any fun this summer, she needed to silence her mom's groans about a sloppy room. Luckily, Meredith was always there to help.

36   What is the main problem Meredith faces in this story?

    ◯ **A** Meredith's brother and her friend have chores to finish before they can go to the pool.

    ◯ **B** Meredith's brother is asleep, so they can't go to the pool.

    ◯ **C** Amy isn't allowed to go to the pool with Meredith.

    ◯ **D** Amy's mom is at work and can't take her and Amy to the pool.

37   What is the main idea of paragraphs 1 and 2?

    ◯ **A** Meredith's brother doesn't want to go to the wave pool.

    ◯ **B** Meredith's brother likes to sleep so he won't have to do chores.

    ◯ **C** Meredith has to do her chores so she can start her fun summer.

    ◯ **D** Meredith tries to wake up her brother so he can do his chores.

GO ON

38 Which of the following best describes Meredith?

    A   careless

    B   helpful

    C   clumsy

    D   tired

39 What is most likely going to happen over the summer?

    A   Meredith's room will get messy, and she will not be able to go to the pool.

    B   Amy will begin to clean her room every morning.

    C   Meredith will help her messy friend so the two can have fun.

    D   Meredith's brother will help Amy with her chores.

40 Amy is <u>thankful</u> for Meredith's help. This means she –

    A   doesn't want anyone to help her

    B   hopes Meredith will help her soon

    C   doesn't think Meredith will be able to help

    D   is glad to have Meredith's help

41 What step does Meredith take when trying to solve the problem she faces?

    A   She tells her mom she is going to Amy's house, but she goes to the wave pool instead.

    B   She promises Amy's mom that she will clean Amy's room another day.

    C   She offers to help Amy clean her room.

    D   She offers to do her brother's chores.

42 How is Meredith different from Amy?

    A   Meredith is neat and tidy; Amy is messy.

    B   Meredith enjoys the wave pool; Amy does not.

    C   Amy is neat and tidy; Meredith is messy.

    D   Amy has a brother; Meredith does not.

Mathematics

Introduction

In the Mathematics section of the Texas Assessment of Knowledge and Skills (TAKS), you will be asked questions to test what you have learned so far in school. These questions are based on the mathematical skills you have been taught in school through fifth grade. The questions you will answer are not meant to confuse or trick you but are written so you have the best chance to show what you know.

On pages 105-106, you will find a Mathematics Chart. This chart looks like a chart you can use when you take the actual TAKS. Use this chart to help you as you answer the items in Assessments 1 and 2.

Questions I Will Answer on the TAKS

There are two types of questions on the Mathematics TAKS for Grade 5: multiple-choice items and griddable items.

Multiple-choice items have four answer choices, and only one is correct. You may see "Not Here" as an answer choice; mark this choice if none of the other choices correctly answer the question. An example of a multiple-choice item is shown below.

For a griddable item, you mark your answer using numbers. An example of a griddable item is shown below. You write your answer in the boxes at the top of the grid; then, you darken the bubbles to mark the correct number. In the example given, a student has recorded an answer of "316." The numbers are written at the top of the grid, and the bubble for each number is marked below. A decimal point is shown in the last column to help you understand the place value of the numbers you record. If you're not sure how to mark your answer for a griddable item, ask a parent or a teacher to show you.

Multiple-Choice Question

1   Jim found 17 seashells on Monday. On Tuesday, he found twice as many seashells. How many seashells did he find total?

    A 27 seashells

    B 34 seashells

    C 51 seashells

    D 68 seashells

Griddable Item

2   Sarah needs to make 500 cookies for a bake sale. She has already made 184 cookies. How many more cookies does Sarah need to make?

Record your answer in the boxes below and fill in the bubbles. Be sure to use the correct place value.

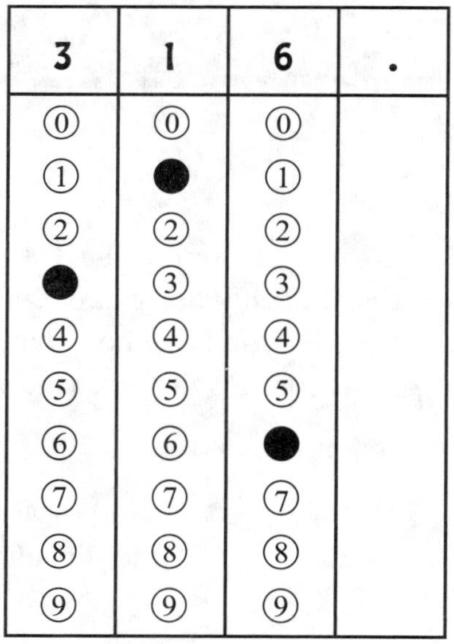

3	1	6	.
⓪	⓪	⓪	
①	●	①	
②	②	②	
●	③	③	
④	④	④	
⑤	⑤	⑤	
⑥	⑥	●	
⑦	⑦	⑦	
⑧	⑧	⑧	
⑨	⑨	⑨	

Grade 5
Mathematics Chart

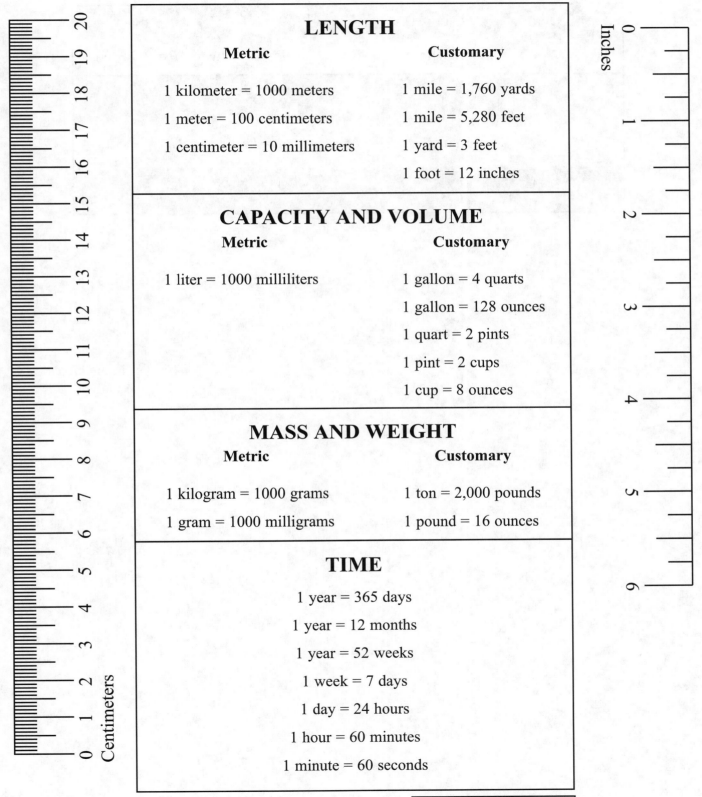

LENGTH

Metric

1 kilometer = 1000 meters

1 meter = 100 centimeters

1 centimeter = 10 millimeters

Customary

1 mile = 1,760 yards

1 mile = 5,280 feet

1 yard = 3 feet

1 foot = 12 inches

CAPACITY AND VOLUME

Metric

1 liter = 1000 milliliters

Customary

1 gallon = 4 quarts

1 gallon = 128 ounces

1 quart = 2 pints

1 pint = 2 cups

1 cup = 8 ounces

MASS AND WEIGHT

Metric

1 kilogram = 1000 grams

1 gram = 1000 milligrams

Customary

1 ton = 2,000 pounds

1 pound = 16 ounces

TIME

1 year = 365 days

1 year = 12 months

1 year = 52 weeks

1 week = 7 days

1 day = 24 hours

1 hour = 60 minutes

1 minute = 60 seconds

Continued on next page

Grade 5 Mathematics Chart

Perimeter	square	$P = 4s$
	rectangle	$P = 2l + 2w$ or $P = 2(l + w)$
Area	square	$A = s^2$
	rectangle	$A = lw$ or $A = bh$
	triangle	$A = \frac{1}{2} bh$ or $A = \frac{bh}{2}$

Directions for Assessment 1

Assessment 1 is made up of multiple-choice questions and griddable items. For a multiple-choice question, fill in one answer bubble to mark the correct answer. For a griddable item, write your answer in the boxes. Then, fill in the bubbles. Be sure to use the correct place value.

Read each question carefully. If you do not know an answer, you may skip the question and come back to it later.

Don't forget that you can use the Mathematics Chart to help you answer the questions.

You will not be permitted to use calculators on this section of the test.

When you finish, check your answers.

1 The table below shows the population of Garden City for each year over a 4-year period.

Year	Population
1997	4,456,369
1998	4,564,369
1999	4,456,639
2000	4,654,369

Which group lists the populations in order from greatest to least?

- **A** 4,564,369; 4,654,369; 4,456,639; 4,456,369
- **B** 4,654,369; 4,564,369; 4,456,639; 4,456,369
- **C** 4,654,369; 4,564,369; 4,456,369; 4,456,639
- **D** 4,654,369; 4,456,639; 4,564,369; 4,456,369

2 During one week in the summer, 13,870,019 people visited an amusement park. Which of the following describes the number of visitors at the amusement park during that week?

- **A** thirteen million eight hundred seventy thousand nineteen hundred
- **B** thirteen eight hundred seventy nineteen
- **C** thirteen million eight hundred seventy thousand nineteen
- **D** thirteen million eight seventy thousand nineteen

3 The fastest speed reached by a jet during a flight was three hundred twenty-nine and twenty-four hundredths. The jet's speed is given in miles per hour. Which of the following describes the fastest speed of the jet?

- **A** 320.924 miles per hour
- **B** 329.024 miles per hour
- **C** 329.24 miles per hour
- **D** 329.204 miles per hour

4 Harvey and his friends entered their pet snails in the 17th Annual Snail Race. The speeds of their snails are listed in miles per hour in the table below.

Snail	Speed (mph)
Bingo	0.031
Slimy	0.029
Gunga	0.04
Roxie	0.009

Which snail is the fastest?

- **A** Bingo
- **B** Slimy
- **C** Gunga
- **D** Roxie

GO ON

5 In Mr. Yamato's class, $\frac{20}{25}$ of the class has brown eyes. Which amount is equivalent to $\frac{20}{25}$?

   ◯ **A** $\frac{1}{5}$

   ◯ **B** $\frac{2}{5}$

   ◯ **C** $\frac{2}{3}$

   ◯ **D** $\frac{4}{5}$

6 Thomas, Theodore, and Abraham were having a puzzle competition. Each of them had 1 hour to put together the same puzzle. Whoever had the most pieces put together correctly at the end of the hour was the winner. At the end of the hour, Thomas had $\frac{3}{5}$ of the puzzle done, Theodore had $\frac{5}{10}$ of the puzzle done, and Abraham had $\frac{9}{25}$ of the puzzle done. Who won the puzzle competition?

   ◯ **A** Thomas

   ◯ **B** Theodore

   ◯ **C** Abraham

   ◯ **D** They each put the same number of pieces together.

GO ON ▶

7　A thousandths cube is shown below.

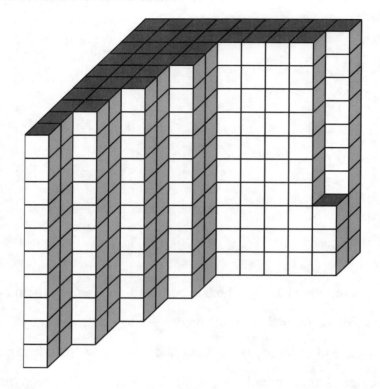

If 0.627 of the cube is missing, what fractional part of the cube is missing?

　A　$\dfrac{6}{27}$

　B　$\dfrac{627}{1,000}$

　C　$6\dfrac{27}{1,000}$

　D　$\dfrac{62.7}{1,000}$

8 There are 645 people at the school fair. Of those 645 people, 417 of them are students. There are also 67 teachers at the fair. The rest of the people at the fair are parents. How many parents are at the school fair?

   ⬭ **A** 128 parents

   ⬭ **B** 161 parents

   ⬭ **C** 228 parents

   ⬭ **D** 295 parents

9 If Jerry delivers 269 newspapers a week, how many newspapers does he deliver in a year?

   ⬭ **A** 13,478 newspapers

   ⬭ **B** 13,878 newspapers

   ⬭ **C** 13,978 newspapers

   ⬭ **D** 13,988 newspapers

10 Sarah works at a candy factory. She can make 690 chocolates in 30 minutes. How many chocolates can she make in 1 minute?

   ⬭ **A** 11.5 chocolates

   ⬭ **B** 13 chocolates

   ⬭ **C** 20.7 chocolates

   ⬭ **D** 23 chocolates

11 The prime factors of 36 are –

   ⬭ **A** 2 x 3 x 3

   ⬭ **B** 2 x 3 x 6

   ⬭ **C** 2 x 2 x 3 x 3

   ⬭ **D** 2 x 2 x 3

12 Felipe is painting blocks of wood for a school project. He has 8 blocks to paint. So far, he has painted the blocks with circles red and the blocks with stars blue. The blocks he has painted are shown below. What fraction of blocks does Felipe have left to paint?

   ⬭ **A** $\dfrac{2}{8}$

   ⬭ **B** $\dfrac{3}{8}$

   ⬭ **C** $\dfrac{5}{8}$

   ⬭ **D** $\dfrac{6}{8}$

GO ON ▶

111

13 Tyrone has a bucket with 22.4 liters of water in it. Oswald has a bottle with 3.7 liters of water in it. Which is a reasonable total number of liters of water that Tyrone and Oswald have?

- **A** less than 20 liters
- **B** between 20 liters and 25 liters
- **C** between 25 liters and 30 liters
- **D** more than 30 liters

14 A group of 4 friends were reading the same book. The person who had read the most had read 31 pages so far. The person who had read the least had read 24 pages so far. Which is a reasonable total number of pages the 4 friends have read?

- **A** less than 60 pages
- **B** between 60 and 90 pages
- **C** between 90 and 120 pages
- **D** more than 120 pages

15 The members of a bird-watching club are adding together how many different types of birds they have seen. James has seen 147 different types of birds that no one else has seen. Robin has seen 61 different types of birds that no one else has seen. Dee Dee has seen only 26 different types of birds that no one else has seen. Which is the best estimate of the total number of different bird types the bird watchers have seen?

- **A** 180 birds
- **B** 200 birds
- **C** 220 birds
- **D** 240 birds

16 Ella had a collection of stamps. She had 129 stamps in her collection. Her uncle sent her his old stamp collection that had the same number of stamps in it as her collection. For her birthday, Ella received 33 new stamps from her friend Daphne and 23 new stamps from her friend Phoebe. Which of the following is the best estimate of how many more stamps Ella got from her uncle than from her friends for her birthday?

- **A** 60 stamps
- **B** 80 stamps
- **C** 200 stamps
- **D** 210 stamps

GO ON

17 Mary's dad is making her a banana split with 3 scoops of ice cream. Each scoop has to be a different flavor. The picture below shows the flavors Mary can use.

How many different combinations of 3 flavors are possible?

Record your answer in the boxes below and fill in the bubbles. Be sure to use the correct place value.

			.
⓪	⓪	⓪	
①	①	①	
②	②	②	
③	③	③	
④	④	④	
⑤	⑤	⑤	
⑥	⑥	⑥	
⑦	⑦	⑦	
⑧	⑧	⑧	
⑨	⑨	⑨	

18 Francis works at a zipper factory. The table below shows how many zippers can be made during different lengths of time. The numbers form a pattern.

Hours	1	2	3	4
Zippers	125	—	375	500

What number is missing from the table?

⬭ **A** 125 zippers

⬭ **B** 150 zippers

⬭ **C** 200 zippers

⬭ **D** 250 zippers

19 Which of the following shows all of the factors of 18?

⬭ **A** 2, 3, 6, 9

⬭ **B** 2, 3, 3

⬭ **C** 1, 2, 3, 6, 9, 18

⬭ **D** 1, 2, 3, 4, 6, 9, 18

GO ON ▶

20 Yoshi wanted to know what his average score was on the 3 spelling tests he had taken. His scores were 95, 97, and 94. Which number sentence should Yoshi use to find the average score of the 3 spelling tests?

A $(95 + 97 + 94) \div 3$

B $(95 \times 3) + (97 \times 3) + (94 \times 3)$

C $(95 + 97 + 94) \times 3$

D $(95 + 97 - 94) \div 3$

21 A large container was being filled with water. The container was 60 feet high. If the water level rose 10 feet every hour, which diagram represents the water level after 3 hours?

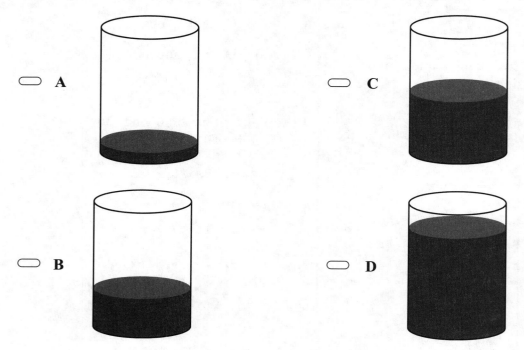

A

C

B

D

22 Ursula and Sharon were baking cookies. They baked a total of 18 dozen cookies (1 dozen = 12 cookies). They took 100 cookies to their teachers. They gave 84 cookies away to friends. Their friend, Maggie, gave Ursula and Sharon 10 cookies each. Which number sentence could be used to find the total number of cookies Ursula and Sharon have now?

A $(18 \times 12) - 100 - 84 + 10$

B $(18 \times 12) - 100 - 84 + (2 \times 10)$

C $(18 - 100 + 84 + 10) \times 12$

D Not Here

23 Which of the following is **NOT** seen in the square below?

- ⬭ **A** right angles
- ⬭ **B** parallel lines
- ⬭ **C** obtuse angles
- ⬭ **D** perpendicular lines

24 Look at the square pyramid shown below.

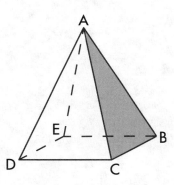

Which statement about the square pyramid is true?

- ⬭ **A** Edge AB is congruent to edge AE.
- ⬭ **B** Edge AB is congruent to edge CD.
- ⬭ **C** Face ABC is congruent to face BCDE.
- ⬭ **D** Face ABE is not congruent to face ACD.

25 Look at the shapes below.

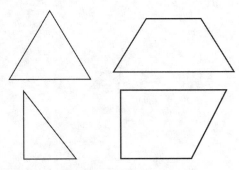

Which shape has all of the following: perpendicular lines, congruent sides, and at least 1 acute angle?

- ⬭ **A**
- ⬭ **B**
- ⬭ **C**
- ⬭ **D**

26 Which solid has the greatest number of vertices?

- ⬭ **A** sphere
- ⬭ **B** square pyramid
- ⬭ **C** cube
- ⬭ **D** triangular prism

GO ON ➡

27 Figures that are symmetrical have halves that are reflections of each other. Which figure is symmetrical?

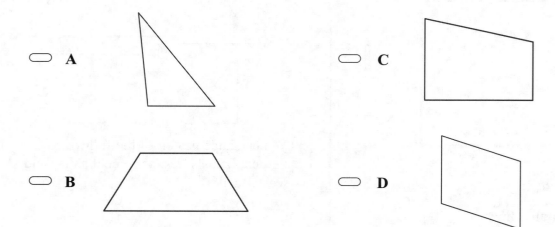

○ A

○ B

○ C

○ D

28 Leah wants to create a rotation of figure RSTU. So far, she has drawn WXY.

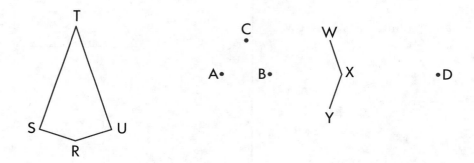

Which point should she use to complete WXY so that it is a rotation of RSTU?

○ **A** Point A

○ **B** Point B

○ **C** Point C

○ **D** Point D

GO ON ➤

29   The unshaded figure on the grid was transformed from the shaded figure.

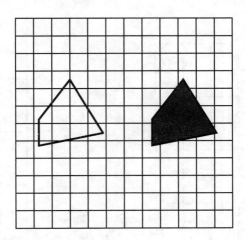

What is the best description of this transformation?

⬭ **A**   rotation

⬭ **B**   reflection

⬭ **C**   translation

⬭ **D**   factorization

30   Which diagram shows a rotation?

⬭ **A**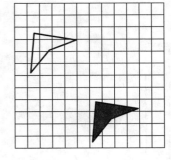

⬭ **C**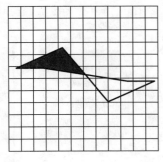

⬭ **B**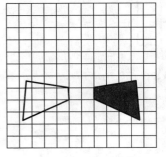

⬭ **D**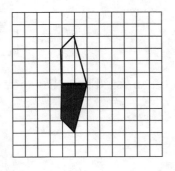

GO ON ➤

31 Fritz created a diagram of his town using a graph.

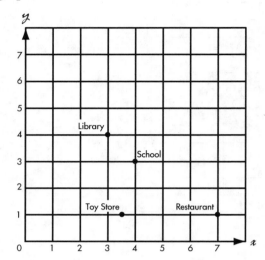

What is located at the ordered pair (4, 3)?

   A School

   B Library

   C Toy Store

   D Restaurant

32 The graph shows the location of some cities.

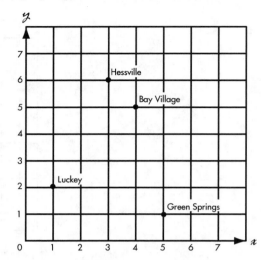

Which city is **NOT** listed with the correct ordered pair location?

   A Green Springs; (5, 1)

   B Luckey; (1, 2)

   C Bay Village; (4, 5)

   D Hessville; (6, 3)

33 Patch Pete, the pirate, hid his treasure using this map.

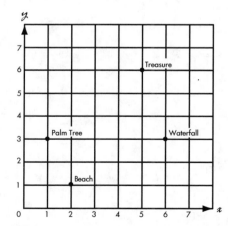

What is the ordered pair that shows where Patch Pete buried his treasure?

   A (6, 5)

   B (2, 1)

   C (4, 5)

   D (5, 6)

34 A rectangular prism made of 1-meter cubes is shown below.

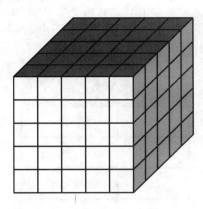

What is the volume of the prism in cubic meters (m³)?

Record your answer in the boxes below and fill in the bubbles. Be sure to use the correct place value.

			.
⓪	⓪	⓪	
①	①	①	
②	②	②	
③	③	③	
④	④	④	
⑤	⑤	⑤	
⑥	⑥	⑥	
⑦	⑦	⑦	
⑧	⑧	⑧	
⑨	⑨	⑨	

35 A rectangular prism made of 1-inch cubes is shown below.

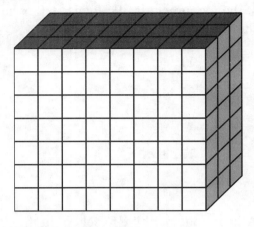

What is the volume of the rectangular prism?

⬭ **A** 168 in.²

⬭ **B** 168 in.³

⬭ **C** 192 in.²

⬭ **D** 192 in.³

36 Each of the rectangular prisms shown below is made of 1-centimeter cubes.

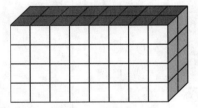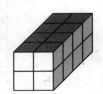

What is the total volume of the 2 rectangular prisms?

⬭ **A** 64 cm³

⬭ **B** 72 cm³

⬭ **C** 96 cm³

⬭ **D** Not Here

GO ON ➤

37 Kareem is building a model of a monument. The monument is 3 times as tall as it is wide. If the monument is 396 inches tall, what is the width of the monument in **feet**?

- **A** 11 feet
- **B** 33 feet
- **C** 99 feet
- **D** 132 feet

38 Allison rode her bike to school in the morning. She left home at 8:00 a.m. and arrived at school at 8:15 a.m. At 3:15 p.m., school was over, and she rode her bike to the library with her friends. They arrived at the library at 3:35 p.m. She left the library at 5:15 p.m. and arrived home for dinner at 5:50 p.m. What is the total number of minutes Allison rode her bike that day?

Record your answer in the boxes below and fill in the bubbles. Be sure to use the correct place value.

			.
⓪	⓪	⓪	
①	①	①	
②	②	②	
③	③	③	
④	④	④	
⑤	⑤	⑤	
⑥	⑥	⑥	
⑦	⑦	⑦	
⑧	⑧	⑧	
⑨	⑨	⑨	

39 Keiko needed to find something to hold 10 gallons of water. The table below lists the things she found that she thought might hold 10 gallons of water. Which object holds exactly 10 gallons?

Object	Capacity
Pitcher	56 pints
Bowl	20 quarts
Vase	160 cups
Sink	1,408 ounces

- **A** pitcher
- **B** bowl
- **C** vase
- **D** sink

40 What unit of measurement is $\frac{1}{7}$ of a week?

- **A** month
- **B** day
- **C** hour
- **D** second

41 Charlie has a bag of candy. In the bag are 12 pieces of candy. He takes 6 pieces of candy from the bag without looking and finds 2 cherry-flavored pieces. Based on those results, what is the probability that Charlie will get a cherry-flavored piece if he takes another piece from the bag?

- A $\frac{1}{2}$

- B $\frac{1}{3}$

- C $\frac{2}{3}$

- D $\frac{3}{4}$

42 Doug wants to earn a medal for swimming at camp. He needs to swim 2 laps in 5 minutes to earn the medal. He practices and keeps track of how many times he is able to swim 2 laps in 5 minutes. Out of 30 practice swims, he is only successful 5 times. Based on these results, what is the probability that Doug will **NOT** earn the swimming medal on his first try?

- A $\frac{1}{25}$

- B $\frac{1}{6}$

- C $\frac{5}{8}$

- D $\frac{5}{6}$

43 A box of animal crackers has 8 different types of animals in it. Miranda takes 8 animal crackers out of the box and finds 3 lions. If the box of animal crackers has 32 crackers in it total, how many lions should Miranda expect to find in the box based on these results?

- A 7 lions

- B 9 lions

- C 12 lions

- D 18 lions

44 The weatherman said there is a 30% chance of rain for today. This is the same as saying the probability of rain is $\frac{3}{10}$. If the chance of rain remains the same for an entire month, how many days out of the month would you expect it to rain?

- A 3 days

- B 9 days

- C 15 days

- D 21 days

GO ON

45 The table shows the coordinates of the points of a line graph.

Point	x	y
A	2	5
B	4	2
C	4	3
D	6	1

Which graph represents the coordinates given in the table above?

○ **A**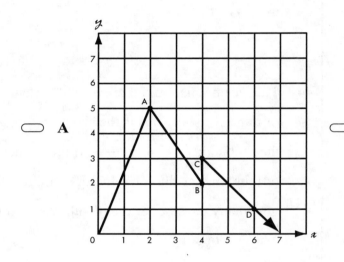

○ **C**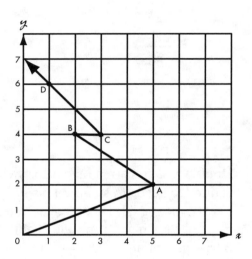

○ **B**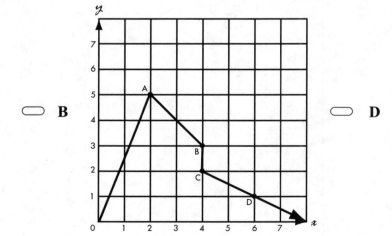

○ **D**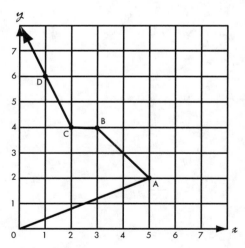

46   Mr. Kent timed some of his students in gym class. Each of the students ran 1 mile. Their times
      are listed on the table.

Name	Time
Clark	6.5 minutes
Pete	7.25 minutes
Chloe	7.5 minutes
Lionel	8.5 minutes
Lana	7.0 minutes

What is the median of the times?

⬭ **A** 2 minutes

⬭ **B** 6.5 minutes

⬭ **C** 7.0 minutes

⬭ **D** 7.25 minutes

GO ON ▶

47 The fifth-grade classes at Polk Elementary School held a contest to see which class could collect the greatest number of pounds of materials to recycle. The results of the contest are listed on the chart.

Class	Pounds
Mr. Nutter	150
Ms. Rodriguez	200
Mrs. Len	225

Which is the most appropriate graph of the information shown in the chart?

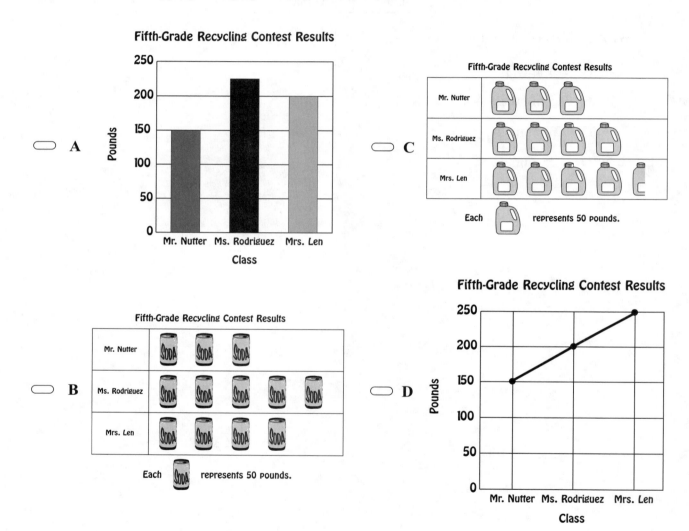

© 2003 Englefield & Associates, Inc.

48 It takes 1 day for 1 inch of snow to melt in Moosehead. The snow only melts on days when it does not snow at all. On Friday, it snowed a total of 7 inches. It did not start to snow again until Monday. On Monday, it snowed 4 inches. If it did not snow any after Monday, how much snow was left on the ground after Wednesday?

  ◯ **A** 1 inch

  ◯ **B** 3 inches

  ◯ **C** 5 inches

  ◯ **D** 7 inches

49 Trudy is 3 years older than twice her brother Kevin's age. If Kevin is 4 years old, how can you figure out how old Trudy is?

  ◯ **A** Multiply 4 by 2, and then add 3.

  ◯ **B** Multiply 4 by 2, and then subtract 3.

  ◯ **C** Add 4 to 3, and then multiply by 2.

  ◯ **D** Subtract 3 from 4, and then multiply by 2.

50 Mrs. Drew asked her students to select 4 blocks from a group of blocks. The 4 blocks had to follow a pattern. Francisco picked the 3 blocks shown below. A block that did not fit the pattern he chose is also shown.

Part of the Pattern

Not Part of the Pattern

Which block should Francisco choose to complete his set of 4 blocks?

◯ **A**

◯ **C**

◯ **B**

◯ **D**

GO ON ▶

51 Last weekend, Alexander's Pizza made 1,819 pizzas but did not sell 12 of them. This weekend, Alexander's Pizza made 1,801 pizzas and sold all but 39 of them. How many more pizzas did Alexander's Pizza sell last weekend?

Record your answer in the boxes below and fill in the bubbles. Be sure to use the correct place value.

			.
⓪	⓪	⓪	
①	①	①	
②	②	②	
③	③	③	
④	④	④	
⑤	⑤	⑤	
⑥	⑥	⑥	
⑦	⑦	⑦	
⑧	⑧	⑧	
⑨	⑨	⑨	

52 Humphrey had a lemonade stand. For each pitcher of lemonade, he used 4 lemons. He bought 30 lemons at the store. If Humphrey made 6 pitchers of lemonade, which number sentence could be used to find L, the number of lemons he had left after he made the 6 pitchers of lemonade?

    A $L = 30 \div 4$

    B $L = 30 - (6 + 4)$

    C $L = 30 - 6(4)$

    D $L = 30 - 4$

53 Jessica is 6 years older than half of her sister Michelle's age. If Michelle is 10 years old, which of the following statements is true?

    A Jessica is older than Michelle.

    B Jessica is younger than Michelle.

    C Jessica and Michelle are the same age.

    D Jessica is 16 years old.

GO ON ▶

54   Mr. Brown wrote the following numbers on the board for his math class: 2, 3, 5, and 7. Which of the following generalizations can be made about the numbers?

   ◯ **A**   They are odd numbers.

   ◯ **B**   They are factors of 70.

   ◯ **C**   They are multiples of 70.

   ◯ **D**   They are prime numbers.

---

55   A poll of students' favorite colors was taken. The results from the poll are shown in the graph below. Yoko looked at the graph and said, "At least 30 students like each color best."

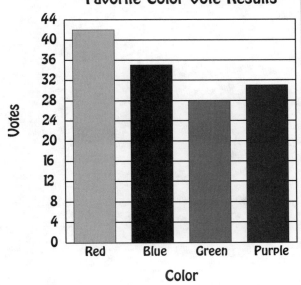

Which statement uses information from the graph to support Yoko or to show that Yoko's generalization is incorrect?

   ◯ **A**   The total number of votes is 136 votes.

   ◯ **B**   More students chose blue than red.

   ◯ **C**   Fewer students chose green than purple.

   ◯ **D**   Only 28 students chose green.

56   A group of friends collects seashells. The number of shells in each of their collections is shown in the table below. The number of seashells is listed starting with the person with the fewest seashells and ending with the person with the most seashells.

Name	Seashells
Maurice	13
Eddie	27
Jim	
Keith	41
Archie	45

Which of the following statements could describe the number of seashells Jim has in his collection?

   ◯ **A**   fewer than 13 seashells

   ◯ **B**   between 13 and 27 seashells

   ◯ **C**   at least 27 seashells

   ◯ **D**   more than 45 seashells

STOP

Directions for Assessment 2

Assessment 2 is made up of multiple-choice questions and griddable items. For a multiple-choice question, fill in one answer bubble to mark the correct answer. For a griddable item, write your answer in the boxes. Then, fill in the bubbles. Be sure to use the correct place value.

Read each question carefully. If you do not know an answer, you may skip the question and come back to it later.

Don't forget that you can use the Mathematics Chart to help you answer the questions.

You will not be permitted to use calculators on this section of the test.

When you finish, check your answers.

1   A group of friends wanted to see who could blow the largest bubble. Their results are shown in the table below.

Name	Bubble Size
Joe	20.5 cm
Titus	15.9 cm
Molly	20.08 cm
Isabel	19.79 cm

Who won the bubble-blowing contest?

    A   Joe

    B   Titus

    C   Molly

    D   Isabel

2   Each student in the fifth grade at Alamo Elementary School is given a package of 16 pencils. If there are 87 students in the fifth grade, what is the total number of pencils they receive?

    A   602 pencils

    B   692 pencils

    C   1,292 pencils

    D   1,392 pencils

3   Trucks that weigh more than 16 tons total are not allowed to drive on Huckleberry Street. Kevin's truck weighs 10,000 pounds. He is carrying 8,000 pounds of cargo. Which statement is true based on this information?

    A   Kevin will be able to drive his truck on Huckleberry Street because his truck weighs 18 tons total.

    B   Kevin will not be able to drive his truck on Huckleberry Street because his truck weighs 18 tons total.

    C   Kevin will be able to drive his truck on Huckleberry Street because his truck weighs 9 tons total.

    D   Kevin will not be able to drive his truck on Huckleberry Street because his truck weighs 9 tons total.

GO ON

4 Look at the figure below.

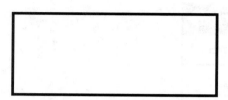

Which statement about this figure is true?

    A The figure contains no parallel lines.

    B The figure contains 4 congruent angles.

    C The figure contains no perpendicular lines.

    D The figure contains 4 congruent sides.

5 Mr. Wilson's class was having a pizza party. They ordered 5 large pizzas and 1 extra-large pizza. A large pizza has 8 pieces. An extra-large pizza has 12 pieces. Which number sentence can be used to find the total number of pieces of pizza Mr. Wilson's class ordered?

    A 6 x 8

    B (5 + 1) x 8

    C 5 x 8 + 12

    D (5 x 8) + 1

6 Eve kept track of how many inches it snowed every day for 1 week. Her results are shown in the table below.

Day	Snow
Monday	2 in.
Tuesday	1 in.
Wednesday	0 in.
Thursday	0 in.
Friday	1/2 in.
Saturday	3 in.
Sunday	0 in.

Based on these results, what is the probability that it will snow tomorrow?

    A $\dfrac{1}{7}$

    B $\dfrac{2}{7}$

    C $\dfrac{3}{7}$

    D $\dfrac{4}{7}$

GO ON

7 Mrs. Duncan decided to build 4 new flower beds in her garden. She bought 420 pounds of topsoil to fill them with. Each of the flower beds needed 88 pounds of topsoil. She also used 54 pounds of topsoil in other parts of her garden. Which number sentence can be used to find T, the number of pounds of topsoil Mrs. Duncan had left?

⬭ **A** $T = 420 - (88 + 54) \times 4$

⬭ **B** $T = 420 - (88 \times 4) - 54$

⬭ **C** $T = (420 - 88 - 54) \times 4$

⬭ **D** $T = 420 - (88 \times 4) + 54$

8 Ms. Hiroshi gave her students 2 lists to choose a snack from. The first list had snack foods on it. The other had snack drinks on it. They were allowed to choose 1 item from each list. How many combinations are possible?

Snack Foods		Snack Drinks	
Chips	🟫	Juice	🧃
Cookie	🍪	Milk	🥛
Apple	🍎		

⬭ **A** 4

⬭ **B** 6

⬭ **C** 10

⬭ **D** 16

9 A rectangular prism made of 1-mile cubes is shown below.

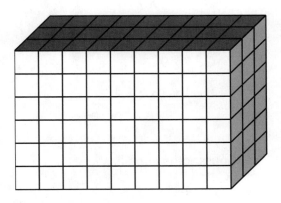

What is the volume of the prism in cubic miles (mi.^{3})?

Record your answer in the boxes below and fill in the bubbles. Be sure to use the correct place value.

			.
⓪	⓪	⓪	
①	①	①	
②	②	②	
③	③	③	
④	④	④	
⑤	⑤	⑤	
⑥	⑥	⑥	
⑦	⑦	⑦	
⑧	⑧	⑧	
⑨	⑨	⑨	

GO ON ▶

10 What are the prime factors of 63?

    ⬭ **A** 3 x 3 x 7

    ⬭ **B** 3 x 21

    ⬭ **C** 7 x 9

    ⬭ **D** 3 x 3 x 3 x 4

11 A thousandths cube is shown below.

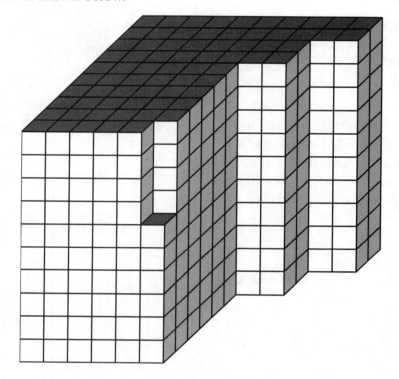

If 0.284 of the cube is missing, what fractional part of the cube is left?

    ⬭ **A** $\dfrac{7}{16}$

    ⬭ **B** $\dfrac{284}{1,000}$

    ⬭ **C** $\dfrac{716}{1,000}$

    ⬭ **D** Not Here

12 The graph below shows the quantity of each type of sports equipment that is in the school gym.

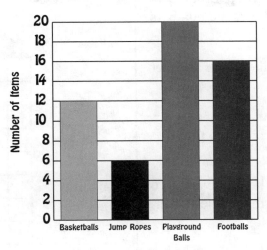

Sports Equipment in the School Gym

What is the range of the number of items?

◯ **A** 6

◯ **B** 14

◯ **C** 20

◯ **D** 54

13 In which diagram is the unshaded figure a reflection of the shaded figure?

◯ **A**
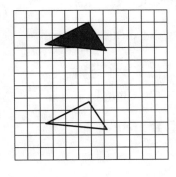

◯ **C**
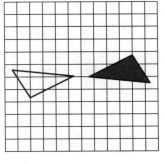

◯ **B**
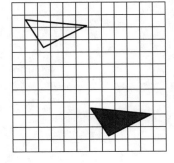

◯ **D**
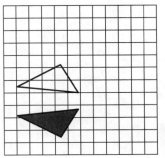

GO ON

14 Mr. Fischaber gave his math class this group of numbers: 2, 5, 8. He asked them to make a generalization about the group of numbers. Which generalization describes the numbers in the group?

    A The numbers in the group are even factors of 80.

    B The numbers in the group are factors of 80 that are also prime numbers.

    C The numbers in the group are all of the factors of 80 that are less than 12.

    D The numbers in the group are factors of 80.

15 Which of the following is the same as $3\frac{1}{2}$ pints?

    A $\frac{1}{2}$ gallon

    B $2\frac{3}{4}$ quarts

    C 7 cups

    D 48 ounces

16 The rectangular prism below is made of 1-inch cubes.

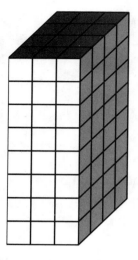

What is the volume of the rectangular prism?

    A 96 cubic inches

    B 84 cubic inches

    C 72 cubic inches

    D 56 cubic inches

17 Which shape has both parallel sides and perpendicular sides?

    A circle

    B triangle

    C sphere

    D rectangle

18 Last week, Colleen had dance practice on 5 days. Usually, dance practice lasts from 7:00 p.m. to 8:30 p.m. On Tuesday, dance practice lasted an hour longer than usual. On Wednesday, Colleen went to the library before dance practice, from 6:30 p.m. to 7:00 p.m. Which steps does Colleen need to follow to find the total number of minutes she spent at dance practice last week?

  A Find the number of minutes from 7:00 p.m. to 8:30 p.m. Multiply that number by 5. Add 60 minutes to that number. Add another 30 minutes to that number.

  B Find the number of minutes from 7:00 p.m. to 8:30 p.m. Multiply that number by 5. Add 60 minutes to that number.

  C Find the number of minutes from 7:00 p.m. to 8:30 p.m. Add 60 minutes to that number.

  D Find the number of minutes from 7:00 p.m. to 8:30 p.m. Add 60 minutes to that number. Multiply that number by 5.

19 Mr. Solari won the lottery. He received a check for 27,019,863 dollars. Which describes the amount of money Mr. Solari won?

  A twenty-seven million nineteen hundred thousand eight hundred sixty-three dollars

  B twenty-seven million one hundred ninety thousand eight hundred sixty-three dollars

  C twenty-seven million nineteen thousand eight hundred sixty-three dollars

  D twenty-seven nineteen eight hundred sixty-three dollars

20 What is the greatest whole number factor of 100?

Record your answer in the boxes below and fill in the bubbles. Be sure to use the correct place value.

21   The figure shown below is a rectangular prism. Which statement about the figure is true?

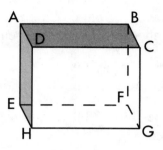

    ◯ **A** Face BCGF is congruent to face ABCD.

    ◯ **B** Face CDHG is congruent to face BAEF.

    ◯ **C** Face ADHE is congruent to face ABFE.

    ◯ **D** Face EFGH is congruent to face DCGH.

22   Maria has 6 boxes that can each hold only 71 books. She has 7 shelves of books that she needs to pack in boxes. Each shelf holds 61 books. Maria thinks she will be able to fit all her books into the boxes she has. Explain why Maria is correct or not.

    ◯ **A** She is correct; the books will fit into 6 boxes with space for more books.

    ◯ **B** She is correct; the books will fit into 6 boxes with no extra space.

    ◯ **C** She is correct; the books will fit into 5 boxes with no extra space.

    ◯ **D** She is incorrect; Maria will need 1 more box to pack all of her books.

23   There are 15 trees in Stacey's backyard. Of those trees, $\frac{9}{15}$ of them are pine trees. Which is the same as $\frac{9}{15}$?

    ◯ **A** $\frac{3}{5}$

    ◯ **B** $\frac{1}{3}$

    ◯ **C** $\frac{6}{9}$

    ◯ **D** $\frac{5}{6}$

24 What is the perimeter of the business card shown below? Use the ruler on the Mathematics Chart to measure in inches.

Crazy Harry's
Party Supplies

6344 Robinbrook Blvd.
Amityville, TX 78888

555-PHUN

⬭ **A** $5\frac{1}{2}$ inches

⬭ **B** 7 inches

⬭ **C** $10\frac{1}{2}$ inches

⬭ **D** 11 inches

25 Mr. Gregory's garden contains 47 flowers. Each flower has about 9 petals. What is a reasonable estimate of the total number of petals in Mr. Gregory's garden?

⬭ **A** fewer than 400 petals

⬭ **B** between 400 and 500 petals

⬭ **C** between 500 and 750 petals

⬭ **D** more than 750 petals

GO ON ➤

26   Dexter made a map of his backyard using a coordinate grid.

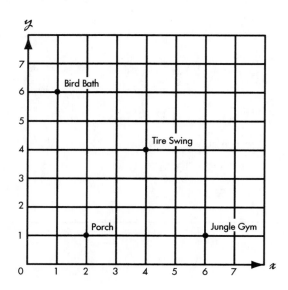

Which item listed below has the correct ordered pair?

⬭   **A**   Bird Bath; (6, 1)

⬭   **B**   Porch; (2, 1)

⬭   **C**   Tire Swing; (3, 3)

⬭   **D**   Jungle Gym; (1, 6)

27   The table below shows how many patients Dr. Monroe sees in 1 day. The numbers form a pattern.

Days	Patients
2	82
4	164
7	287
9	369
11	451

How many patients will Dr. Monroe see in 12 days?

⬭   **A**   472 patients

⬭   **B**   482 patients

⬭   **C**   492 patients

⬭   **D**   502 patients

28 A flock of 29 birds was flying south for the winter. They could fly 21 miles in 1 hour. Which is the best estimate of how many miles they could travel in 7 hours?

    A   140 miles

    B   170 miles

    C   220 miles

    D   290 miles

29 Look at the line graph below.

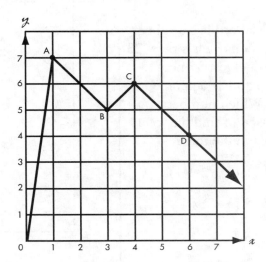

Which table represents the coordinates of the points on the line graph?

A

Point	x	y
A	1	7
B	3	5
C	4	6
D	6	4

C

Point	x	y
A	7	1
B	5	3
C	6	4
D	4	6

B

Point	x	y
A	1	7
B	3	5
C	4	6
D	6	3

D

Point	x	y
A	7	1
B	5	3
C	6	4
D	3	6

GO ON

30 In 1 month, Rita read 3 books that each had 130 pages and 1 book with 273 pages. Which number sentence below can be used to find *P*, the total number of pages Rita read that month?

◯ **A** $P = (273 + 130) \times 3$

◯ **B** $P = (273 - 130) \times 3$

◯ **C** $P = 273 + 3(130)$

◯ **D** $P = (273 + 130) \times 2$

31 Every year the town of Mallard has a rubber ducky race in the river. In this year's race, 23 people entered 3 rubber duckies, 57 people entered 2 rubber duckies, and 106 people entered 1 rubber ducky. Which number sentence below can be used to find the total number of rubber duckies in the race?

◯ **A** $(23 + 57 + 106) \times (3 + 2 + 1)$

◯ **B** $(23 + 57 + 106) \times (3 \times 2 \times 1)$

◯ **C** $(23 + 57 + 106) \times 2$

◯ **D** $(23 \times 3) + (57 \times 2) + 106$

32 A large piñata was brought in for a class party. The piñata was filled with 841 pieces of candy. If each of the 29 students in the class got the same amount of candy, how many pieces of candy did each student receive?

Record your answer in the boxes below and fill in the bubbles. Be sure to use the correct place value.

			.
⓪	⓪	⓪	
①	①	①	
②	②	②	
③	③	③	
④	④	④	
⑤	⑤	⑤	
⑥	⑥	⑥	
⑦	⑦	⑦	
⑧	⑧	⑧	
⑨	⑨	⑨	

GO ON

---

33 Trevor was given the following figures and was told they have something in common.

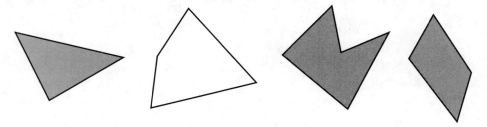

Which of the following statements explains why Figure X belongs with the other figures?

Figure X

⬭ **A** It is shaded.

⬭ **B** It has an even number of sides.

⬭ **C** It has fewer than 6 sides.

⬭ **D** It is not a triangle.

34 Elliot took a handful of candy from a bag. In his hand, he had 7 yellow pieces of candy, 9 red pieces of candy, 4 orange pieces of candy, and 8 brown pieces of candy. Based on this information, if Elliot had only taken 1 piece of candy from the bag, what color would it most likely have been?

⬭ **A** yellow

⬭ **B** red

⬭ **C** orange

⬭ **D** brown

35 Which group shows the complete set of whole number factors of a composite number?

⬭ **A** 1, 19

⬭ **B** 1, 3, 4, 12

⬭ **C** 1, 2, 4, 8, 16

⬭ **D** 1, 2, 5, 10, 20

36 Chang wants to buy a magazine. He has $10.00. He knows the magazine costs $4.95. When he buys the magazine, he is charged $0.28 in sales tax. Which of the number sentences below can be used to find the amount of money Chang has after he buys the magazine?

⬭ **A** $10.00 – $4.95

⬭ **B** $10.00 – ($4.95 x $0.28)

⬭ **C** $10.00 – $4.95 + $0.28

⬭ **D** $10.00 – ($4.95 + $0.28)

37 Edson drew a model of the soccer field on the school playground. The scale he used is given with the diagram of the soccer field below.

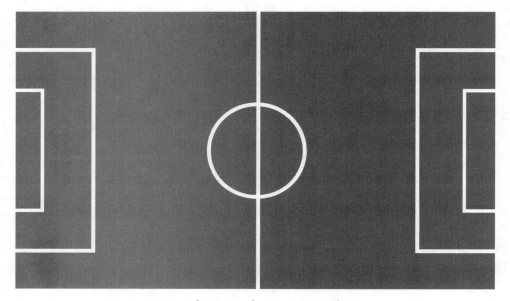

Scale: 1 inch = 20 yards

What is the area of the real soccer field in square yards? Use the ruler on the Mathematics Chart to measure in inches.

⬭ **A** 15 square yards

⬭ **B** 600 square yards

⬭ **C** 1,200 square yards

⬭ **D** 6,000 square yards

38 The coordinate grid below shows where some of the boys in Mrs. Ross's class sit.

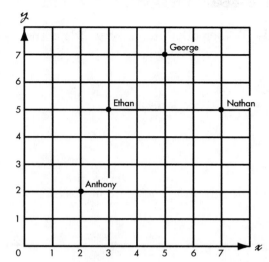

Who sits at the ordered pair (5, 7)?

     A Anthony

     B George

     C Nathan

     D Ethan

39 Dan works at a bookstore 3 nights a week after school. He makes $6.00 an hour. If he wants to know how much money he will make in a year, what other information does he need to know?

     A how many nights during the week he doesn't work

     B how many customers he helps every hour

     C how many books are in the bookstore

     D how many hours he works each night

40 The rectangular prism below is made of 1-meter cubes.

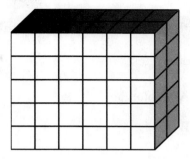

What is the volume of the rectangular prism?

     A 60 m^3

     B 52 m^3

     C 41 m^3

     D 32 m^3

41 Look at the square pyramid below.

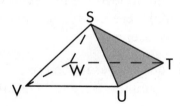

Which statement about the square pyramid is true?

     A Angle TUV is an obtuse angle.

     B Angle TUV is an acute angle.

     C Angle TUV is a right angle.

     D There is no way to tell what type of angle Angle TUV is.

GO ON

42 A group of friends was comparing how each of them did on a spelling test. Yolanda spelled $\frac{4}{5}$ of the words correctly. Sid spelled $\frac{7}{10}$ of the words correctly. Eric spelled $\frac{3}{4}$ of the words correctly. Ulysses spelled $\frac{17}{20}$ of the words correctly. Who spelled the most words correctly on the spelling test?

- **A** Yolanda

- **B** Sid

- **C** Eric

- **D** Ulysses

43 Uther owns a table factory. To celebrate a large order, Uther bought 7 packages of pens with a dragon logo on them. Each package contained 212 pens. He added the pens to the 373 pens he already had. Then, he gave 419 pens each to his children Arthur, Lance, and Gwen. Of the pens he had left, he kept 12 for himself and divided the rest evenly among his 12 employees. How many pens did each employee receive?

Record your answer in the boxes below and fill in the bubbles. Be sure to use the correct place value.

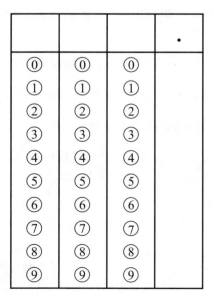

44 At summer camp, campers kept track of the total number of laps they swam in the pool. At the end of the summer, they put the information into the bar graph shown below. Bruce said, "We all swam over 20 laps!" Which statement shows why Bruce's generalization is incorrect?

Total Laps Swam During Summer Camp

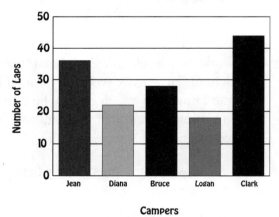

- **A** Clark swam twice as many laps as Diana.

- **B** Bruce swam the median number of laps.

- **C** Logan swam 18 laps.

- **D** Jean swam more laps than Bruce.

Student Notes

Thank You
For Your Purchase!

For more information on TAKS products,

call 1-877-PASSING (727-7464), or

visit our websites:

www.showwhatyouknowpublishing.com

www.passthetaks.com